D0363827

THE FRIEND OF JESUS

THE GOSPEL ACCORDING TO
JUDAS ISCARIOT.

11 pt. letter
main leaded

THE FRIEND OF JESUS

BY
ERNEST
SUTHERLAND
BATES

SIMON AND SCHUSTER

NEW YORK : 1928

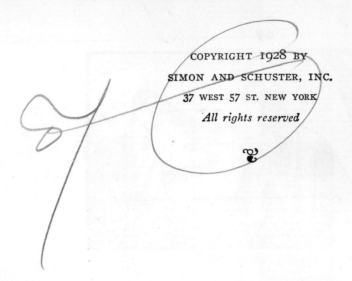

PRINTED IN THE UNITED STATES OF AMERICA
BY THE VAIL-BALLOU PRESS, BINGHAMTON, NEW YORK

Printed in Great Britain at
THE WINDMILL PRESS
Kingswood Surrey

TABLE OF CONTENTS

v

TABLE OF CONTENTS

TABLE OF CONTENTS

THE FRIEND OF JESUS

 *lift in each case.*

I, JUDAS of Kerioth, was the son of Barzillai the son of Nahash, of the tribe of Judah. Nahash was my grandfather called, for he possessed the knowledge of the Serpent, but my father was Barzillai, One Made of Iron. Iron he was to me, and iron to all men.

How Judas was reared among the Essenes

And we dwelt at Kerioth, south from Jerusalem, nigh unto the wilderness of Judea.

And when I was yet a child my mother died, so that I never knew her face.

She it was that named me Judas, meaning One Greatly to be Praised. But it is well that she died, for today my name is spat upon even among the Jews, and it is held accursed by all the followers of Jesus.

Now Barzillai, my father, in after years went out from Kerioth into the wilderness of Judea, and he took me with him, and joined the company of the Essenes, who dwell in the wilderness hard by the Salt Sea.

The same are they from whom John the Baptist later came forth, but at this time he was not yet among them.

How Judas was reared among the Essenes

Now the Essenes worship Jehovah after a purer manner than do the rest of the Jews: for they abhor bloody sacrifices, and their acts are deeds of mercy, and they have all things in common.

Yet they read the Law of Moses many times a day, they neither eat nor drink without prayer, nor are women allowed among them, nor may one speak without permission of his elders, and he who goeth into the fields to work goeth and returneth according to command.

And their fields are poor and scanty, for it is a barren land, a land of death. Miserable is their food, and miserable their clothes, miserable their way of life and the place of it.

For the Salt Sea lieth beneath, and the springs are few, and little rain falleth. There are there no trees to shield one from the hot sun that beateth down; but the land is high and stony, with stretches of sand between, and the sun beateth down without a cloud.

And in the face of the vast wilderness, man seemeth but an ant without an ant-hill.

And my soul dwindled and failed, but Barzillai, my father, was content.

They taught me the Law of Moses, and I

2

hated it; they told me I must worship Jehovah, and I could not.

How Judas was reared among the Essenes

For in the evenings the mountains of Moab in the east were changed into purple, and, far down in the west, a faint line of blue was the sea.

So from the east and the west I heard voices that spake of other men than those about me, and of other gods than Jehovah.

And when I beheld the eagle rejoicing in his wings, or the wild asses running with clouds of dust, I thought, surely, they have a god, but they are happier than I: for they are free, and I am a slave.

Surely their god makes them happy and strong, while Jehovah makes men poor and weak and miserable.

And oftentimes I would go out into the desert and take counsel with the serpents, and with Satan, the prince of the serpents. And they confirmed all that the voices had said in mine own heart.

3

CHAPTER II

AND Satan said unto me:

In the beginning was God, the Unknown God, Ineffable and Unnamed; God of God, Life of Life, Very God of Very God, everchanging yet unchanged, as He was in the beginning, is now, and ever shall be.

He passeth continually into Fire, and Fire passeth into Heat, and Heat into Light, and Light into Ether, and Ether passeth into Matter, and Matter passeth into Mind, and Mind into Air, and Air into Ether, and Ether passeth into Fire once more.

And He created innumerable worlds before this world, and the stars of heaven and the sun and the moon: to endure for a day and a night.

And He created innumerable forms of life in all the worlds, and in all the waste spaces between the worlds: for He was and is and ever shall be Eternal Life.

And He created the earth.

And God said, Let the earth bring forth the living creature after his kind, cattle and

5

How the world was created, according to Satan

creeping thing, and the fowl of the air and the beast of the earth after his kind: and it was so.

And God said, Let us make man in the image of the beast, and yet let him obtain dominion over the fish of the sea, and over the fowl of the air, and over the cattle, and over every creeping thing that creepeth upon the earth.

So God created man in the image of the beast; in the image of the beast created He him; male and female created He them.

And God blessed them, and God said unto them, Be fruitful, and multiply, and replenish the earth, and subdue it: and have dominion over the fish of the sea, and over the fowl of the air, and over every living thing that moveth upon the earth.

Lo, I have given unto you life, and the wary instinct of the beast, and the mind of man, which overcometh the beast; I have given you a tongue wherewith to speak, and lips wherewith to laugh, and eyes wherewith to weep.

And I place Myself within you, even as I am within the herb and the tree and the beasts; yea, even more than within any other beast am I within you.

Seek Me, then, within yourselves: call unto

6

Me and I will reply; plead with Me and I will make answer unto you.

How the world was created, according to Satan

Yet shall every one of you hear My voice in varying wise, for I have given unto every one of you a varying body and a varying soul from that of every other.

Fear not: it is My voice. In finding yourself, ye shall find Me.

Beware of seeking My aid otherwhere. Beware of praying to the fire or the waters or the wind or any star or the immeasurable universe itself. I am in them, but in them I regard you not. Then do ye regard not them, but seek Me only in yourselves.

And make not unto yourselves other gods, to bow down to them and worship them. Bow not down even to Me, but lift up your heads with thanksgiving, even as do the flowers, for I am with you, and I am with them, also.

And God ceased speaking, and His voice was heard no more on earth save as He spoke thenceforward through His prophets, which were many.

CHAPTER III

A<small>ND</small> Satan continued:

Then men said, one unto another: We are alone, and we are afraid. Lo, the fire burneth us, and we drown in the great waters; the winds blow upon us, and destroy us; we are stricken with diseases from the stars. Let us pray unto the fire and the waters, unto the winds and the stars.

So they prayed unto them. But the fire and the waters, the winds and the stars heeded not their prayers. And they suffered from terror by night and from pestilence in the noonday.

Then men said, one unto another: Lo, let us make unto ourselves gods, to protect us from the terror that flieth by night and from the pestilence that walketh in the noonday.

And they made unto them gods, of many forms, and many names. As many peoples as there were upon the earth, so many and more were the gods they made.

And these gods protected them not from the terror by night nor from the pestilence at noonday; but they asserted power over them,

9

and demanded tribute of sacrifice and burnt offerings, and ruled them with a rod of iron that bended not.

Now the most evil of all these gods was named Jehovah: the most evil and tyrannous, a jealous god, a lover of strife and iniquity;

Whose dwelling was among the clouds upon Mount Sinai; but he remained not alway in his dwelling, but went to and fro upon the earth, and walked up and down in it.

And upon a certain day, as this Jehovah was walking upon the earth, far from Mount Sinai, he came unto the Garden of Eden, between the river Tigris and the river Euphrates, where dwelt a man named Adam and a woman named Eve.

Now in this garden grew every tree that is pleasant to the sight and good for food; the tree of life, also, stood in the midst of the garden, and the tree of knowledge of good and evil.

And Jehovah was pleased with the appearance of the garden, and he said, This garden is mine; but he was jealous of the presence of the man, wherefore he called him unto him, and commanded him, saying:

Of every tree of the garden thou mayst

freely eat; but of the tree of knowledge of
good and evil, thou shalt not eat of it: for in
the day that thou eatest thereof thou shalt
surely die.

How Gods were created

Now the spirit of the Unknown God dwelt
in every herb and tree and beast; and above
all it dwelt in the Serpent. For of all living
things the Serpent is most like unto God.

Even as it windeth its way in and out
through the world, so God windeth His way
in and out through every living form, and
even as God changeth His form, so doth the
Serpent change his covering, sloughing off the
old skin when it is worn out, and triumphing
in a new and more resplendent one.

And the Serpent is the most subtle of every
beast of the field. And he liveth alone and is
free; and he hateth Jehovah with an undying
hatred, and feareth him not.

Wherefore the Serpent said unto the
woman, Eve, for he knew that she was possessed of more courage than the man: Yea,
hath Jehovah said, Ye shall not eat of every
tree of the garden?

And the woman said unto the Serpent, We
may eat of the fruit of the trees of the garden:

But of the fruit of the tree which is in the

How Gods were cre-ated midst of the garden, Jehovah hath said, Ye shall not eat of it, neither shall ye touch it, lest on that very day ye die.

And the Serpent said unto the woman: Ye shall not die.

For Jehovah doth know that in the day ye eat thereof, then your eyes shall be open, and ye shall be better than the gods, for ye shall know good and evil.

And when the woman saw that the tree was good for food, and that it was pleasant to the eyes, and a tree to be desired to make one wise, she took of the fruit thereof, and did eat, and gave also unto the man with her, and he did eat.

And the eyes of them both were opened, and they knew that they were naked; and they perceived for the first time the beauty of their flesh, and knew that whatsoever is beautiful is good. Therefore they began a joyous dancing in their nakedness.

CHAPTER IV

AND Satan continued:

Then they perceived for the first time that they loved one another: for love is born of joy and beauty.

And Adam fell to singing: Fair is the day and the night and the many stars of the night, but fairer art thou to me. Thy skin is clear as the lily, and the grace of the leopard is thine also.

Thy breasts are bright as the hills of the morning, and thy long hair is as the waving tree-tops of the forest. Let me wrap me in thy long hair and press me against thy breasts, my Beloved.

And Eve answering sang: Beautiful is the storm and the lightning and the great wind that breaketh the forest, but more beautiful art thou to me. Thy limbs are firm as the oak-tree, and the strength of the panther is thine.

Thou art welcome unto me, as the rain is welcome unto the teeming earth. Descend upon me, as the rain descendeth upon the earth. Hide me in thy strong arms, my Be-

*Why Adam
and Eve
were ex-
pelled from
the Garden
of Eden*

loved, and press thy broad bosom upon my rounded breasts. For from this hour shall spring a race of men to render thanksgiving unto life, from one generation unto another, as long as the world shall last.

Now Jehovah walked in the garden in the cool of the day to see if he might spy upon them. And he heard their voices, and he called unto Adam and said, Where art thou? Hast thou eaten of the tree of knowledge that I hear thee speaking with a voice of happiness?

And the man said, Yea, I have eaten of the tree of knowledge. The woman gave me to eat of the tree, and she hath blessed me. What we have done, that have we done knowingly, and conceived a race which shall be beautiful and free forevermore.

And Jehovah was wroth, and he said unto the woman: Because of this, I will greatly multiply thy sorrow; in sorrow shalt thou bring forth thy children; and thy desire shall be to thy husband, and he shall rule over thee.

Then Eve answered and said unto him: Yea, this is in thy power; but it is not in thy power to prevent me from bringing forth children. And in them shall be my delight, far exceeding any sorrow thou canst send upon me.

14

Behold, thou hast not spoken any new thing, for my desire is now unto my husband, and could not be more for aught that thou canst say.

And whether he shall rule over me, or I over him, or whether neither of us shall rule over the other, this, time only shall know. But I think that the ruling of one by another is more fit for gods than for men.

And Jehovah turned away from her and said unto Adam: Because thou hast eaten of the tree, of which I commanded thee, saying, Thou shalt not eat of it: cursed is the ground for thy sake; in sorrow shalt thou eat of it all the days of thy life;

In the sweat of thy face shalt thou eat bread, till thou return unto the ground; for out of it wast thou taken: for dust thou art, and unto dust shalt thou return.

Then Adam answered and said unto him: Yea, I think that in this thou speakest the truth. Yet hast thou lied to me before, for thou saidst unto me, In the day thou eatest of the tree thou shalt surely die;

But this very day have I eaten of the tree, and yet I live.

Behold, from this day I shall worship thee no longer. Rather would I worship the Ser-

Why Adam and Eve were expelled from the Garden of Eden

15

pent, for he speaketh the truth. But I shall worship neither the Serpent nor thee, nor any other thing which man hath created or hath not created.

For now I know that to live is good, and to be beautiful is good, and to be wise and strong, and to love is good; and there are no other goods than these, either in heaven or upon the earth.

Doth Jehovah think that I am a child, to frighten me with childish words? Because I shall labor and pour the sweat of my face upon the ground, shall life therefore become evil rather than more good? And though I die, shall not my children live?

Then Jehovah said, Behold, the man is become wiser than one of us, for he knoweth good from evil: and now lest he put forth his hand, and take also of the tree of life, and eat, and live forever:

Therefore Jehovah drove him forth from the garden to till the ground; and for the man and the woman he made coats of skin, and did force them to be clad in them, hoping thus to conceal their knowledge of good and evil from themselves.

But ofttimes, when the spirit of the Unknown God came upon them, would they cast off their coats and dance naked dances of joy, even as they had done in the garden. And for long they worshipped neither Jehovah nor the Serpent, nor any other thing which man hath created or hath not created.

Why Adam and Eve were expelled from the Garden of Eden

CHAPTER V

AND Satan continued:

Now the child of their youth was a man-child, and was named Cain, signifying, A man from God: for this child was the pride of their eyes and the joy of their hearts.

And while he was but a youth he aided his parents mightily in the care of the fields and in the tilling of the ground, and he planted vines and fruit-trees, and made a garden like unto the Garden of Eden, and in all things was pleasing unto his parents.

And he worshipped not Jehovah nor regarded him.

But as the years went on, Adam and Eve passed into the autumn of life; the fire of their youth was turned to ashes, and their souls were like an empty hearth.

And they said, Jehovah is stronger than we; let us once more serve him that perchance he may give us to eat of the tree of life, and so we escape death at the last. And little by little they began to sacrifice burnt offerings unto Jehovah.

19

*Why Abel
was killed*

Now Eve had conceived again and had borne a child, Abel, the child of his parents' old age. And Abel was the brother of Cain by birth, but in naught else was he like unto Cain.

For from his youth up he would not have to do with the hard labor of the fields and the vineyards, but he chose the easier lot of leading about the sheep upon the hill-sides.

And he was a seer of visions and a dreamer of dreams. And Jehovah spake unto him in his dreams, saying, Go thou down, and sacrifice unto me my sacrifice. And compel also thy brother Cain to sacrifice unto me, that I may witness of my favor unto thee, and abase him in thy sight.

And Abel led his flocks down from the hills, and builded him an altar in the midst of the plain, and he slew the firstlings of his flock, and made the altar to drip with their blood.

And Abel knelt before the altar and said: Have pity upon thy servant, O Jehovah. I am humbled in the dust before thee, I am nothing; but thou art great. Drink of the blood of these lambs, and know that it is I who offer it to thee, and protect me though I deserve no protection.

And Jehovah was pleased with the words

20

of Abel and had respect unto him and his offering.

Then called Abel unto Cain and said, My brother, thou art sinful. Come and sacrifice, as I have done, unto Jehovah. But Cain answered and said, What have I to do with Jehovah, or he with me?

But his parents urged him to the sacrifice, and Adam said, My son, it will profit us for thee to do so, and Eve said, My son, hast thou no regard for thy mother?

So Cain gathered of the fruit of the garden and of the vineyards, and he held it forth in his hands, standing erect and speaking with a loud voice, saying:

O Jehovah, if thou art a righteous god and not a god of blood, accept this offering on which no blood is sprinkled; accept it not for my sake but for the sake of my father and mother who offer it through me.

But Jehovah was not pleased with the words of Cain, and he had no respect for his offering but dashed it out of his hands upon the ground.

And Abel triumphed over his brother, saying: Lo, did not I say that thou wast sinful? Jehovah is my protection, and thee hath he cast under my feet.

Why Abel
was killed

Then Cain was wroth and answered, Let him protect thee now if he can! And he rushed upon Abel and struggled with him and slew him.

Nor did Jehovah protect Abel, but afterwards he spake unto Cain wrathfully, and said, Where is now thy brother Abel? And Cain answered and said: I know not. Am I my brother's keeper?

For I perceive that there is a war between thy servants and them that will not serve; and it setteth a man at variance against his father, and brother against brother. And every man must be his own keeper henceforward.

Then Jehovah cursed Cain for the sake of Abel, and he said: Henceforward a fugitive and a vagabond shalt thou be in the earth. Yet Cain repented not for the death of Abel, but departed with a firm step from the presence of Jehovah.

CHAPTER VI

A<small>ND</small> Satan continued:

Then Cain was a fugitive and a vagabond in the earth, and he wandered over many lands and saw strange customs of men, so that he acquired much wisdom.

Of Cain's good fortune and of the troubles of Jehovah

Therefore Cain laughed, and said: The curses of Jehovah are more profitable than his blessings: for Abel whom he blessed is dead, while I whom he cursed have seen many lands and acquired much wisdom.

Thus was Cain strengthened for a life full of days and deeds;

Nor knew he when the sun rose where he would be when it set, nor yet cared he to know, for he said:

The earth is my home, and I have brothers among all nations. Wherever the wind bloweth, there find I enemies to smite down and friends to raise up; innumerable are the deeds there are to do.

But when a son was borne unto him by a woman of the land of Nod, then Cain said, Now despite Jehovah will I wander no

*Of Cain's
good for-
tune and of
the troubles
of Jehovah*
longer; meet it is that I rest here, and rear a dwelling for the generations of my children.

And he builded him a strong city, and called the name of the city after his son, Enoch.

And when death came upon him, and in the hour of his death, Cain said, Lo, I have lived long, and every day I have found somewhat for my hand to do. Therefore I die content.

And thereafter the sons of Cain proved themselves to be men wise and powerful, and they dwelt in the unconquerable city of Enoch, the same which was later called Baalbec.

And the daughters of the race of Cain were tall and beautiful to look upon, with full bosoms and broad hips; suitable to be the sisters and the mothers of heroes were the daughters of the race of Cain.

Now Jehovah, whether in lawful wedlock or out of lawful wedlock, had begotten sons, and so likewise had done the other gods.

And it came to pass that these sons of the gods looked upon the daughters of men and saw that they were fair; and they took them wives of all which they chose.

And the daughters of the race of Cain, after the sons of the gods had come in unto them, bare children, and the same became mighty

24

men which were of old, men of renown, and giants.

Of Cain's good fortune and of the troubles of Jehovah

And Jehovah saw that men were waxing great, and he trembled at them, for they worshipped him not at all; and he feared them, and knew not what to do.

And Jehovah sat, revolving this in his mind, for season after season.

CHAPTER VII

AND Satan continued:

Then at last there came a time of great snow upon the mountains, and when the snow melted, the streams rushed down from the mountains like a wall and flooded all the plains thereabouts.

And men were caught in the flood and perished, they and their wives and their children, and the fowls and the cattle which were with them,

Yea, all the people of that part perished, save only one man, his three sons, and the wives of his three sons, who, deserting their kindred, gat them unto the top of Mount Ararat, and were saved.

And Jehovah looked upon this man, whose name was Noah, and beheld that he was an ignorant and foolish man, and Jehovah said unto himself:

Lo, the opportunity is mine. I will go down and speak unto Noah and restore my worship among men henceforward.

So Jehovah went down, and said unto

Of Noah and his curses

Noah: Behold, I, even I, have brought this flood of waters upon the earth to destroy all flesh, wherein is the breath of life, from under heaven; but thee and thy wife, thy sons and thy sons' wives, have I saved, that ye may worship me and make sacrifice unto me.

And Noah answered and said: Lord, was it indeed thou? I had deemed that it was the snow upon the mountains that melted and made the great flood. Now am I indeed glad to know the truth concerning this.

And Jehovah said: Be not deceived, it was I. And let this be for a lesson and a warning unto thee to forsake thy vain knowledge nor to seek after explanations of that which may not be explained. For otherwise I will not hold thee guiltless.

And Noah grovelled upon the ground and said: Lord, be not angry with thy servant. I thought it not of mine own accord; other men told me that the snows upon the mountains had made the flood. Far be it from me to seek for an explanation of aught. And he sacrificed unto Jehovah and worshipped him.

Now this Noah was not alone a foolish man, but he was also a winebibber and a sot. And in the days after the flood he planted a vineyard and made wine, and he drank of the wine, and was drunken.

And in his drunkenness Noah did hurt unto his wife and said foolish things until he sank to sleep and lay uncovered within his tent.

Then Ham, the son of Noah and the father of Canaan, went out and said unto his brethren, Shem and Japhet: Behold, our father Noah is a winebibber and a sot, and he hath beaten our mother and said foolish things, and now he lieth uncovered within the tent. What therefore is to be done?

And Shem and Japhet put their fingers upon their lips, and took a garment, placing it upon both their shoulders, and went backward and covered the nakedness of their father.

And when Noah awakened from his wine they told him all that their brother had said and all that they had done, and besought him to curse their brother.

And Noah answered, Ham I dare not curse for he is a grown man; howbeit, his little son will I curse.

And he said, Cursed be Canaan; a servant of servants shall he be unto his brethren. And blessed be Shem, and Canaan shall be his

29

*Of Noah
and his
curses*

servant. And blessed be Japhet, and Canaan shall be his servant, also.

And when Ham heard of the curse, he said, Yea, this is the lot of him that telleth the truth, and it shall alway be his lot, to be cursed by them that have cause to dread the truth.

And the years passed, but the curses of Noah proved to be of no more effect than the curses of Jehovah; for the descendants of Canaan waxed great in the land,

And builded unto themselves two fair cities, named Sodom and Gomorrah, in the which they worshipped not Jehovah, but were their own gods and did as seemed right in their own eyes; and these cities were filled with dancing, and the people lived in joy.

And Jehovah was vexed and said unto himself, Will men never weary of building cities and becoming sufficient unto themselves and forgetting my worship? Now what am I to do?

And once more he sat, revolving this in his mind, for season after season.

CHAPTER VIII

AND Satan continued:

Then at last there came a time of earthquake and fire, and the mountains heaved up their bowels, and poured down lava and brimstone upon Sodom and Gomorrah, and destroyed them utterly.

And Jehovah was glad, for he beheld but two men left alive, named Abraham and Lot, which had fled from the cities, and now stood beside a pillar of salt, gazing back. For Lot remembered his wife, whom he had left behind, and was for returning, but Abraham sought to dissuade him.

And Jehovah descended, and said unto Lot: I have destroyed the cities of Sodom and Gomorrah; and thy wife, because she lingered too long, have I turned into yonder pillar of salt. Therefore think not of her, but go thy ways and worship me.

And the men trembled, and said, Yea, Lord, thy ways are true and righteous altogether. And they worshipped Jehovah.

But shortly thereafter the two quarrelled

31

Of Jeho-vah's idea of father-hood

and separated, and Abraham took unto him-self a wife from another people, and they journeyed together even into Egypt.

And when they were come into Egypt, Abraham was sore afraid, for Sarah his wife was a fair woman to look upon, and he feared lest the Egyptians should slay him because of her.

Wherefore he gave it out that she was his sister, and said no word when she was taken to be Pharaoh's concubine. But when Pharaoh went in unto her and found that she was no longer a virgin, he was very wroth: for he de-sired none but virgins.

So Pharaoh cast Sarah out of his house, and she and Abraham returned quickly once more into the country of the north.

Now Abraham had given unto Sarah an Egyptian handmaid named Hagar, that was pleasing in his eyes; and Sarah bare him no children, but Hagar the Egyptian conceived, and bare him a son, Ishmael.

Then Jehovah was much grieved that his servant, Abraham, should have begotten a son out of lawful wedlock and none other; and Jehovah had much faith in the seed of man; wherefore Jehovah said unto Abraham:

Now will I bless Sarah, and give thee a son

also of her: yea, I will bless her, and she shall be a mother of nations, and a father of nations shalt thou be, for thou art my servant, Abraham. Therefore, even if thy wife seemeth barren, I say unto thee, Persevere.

Of Jehovah's idea of fatherhood

So Abraham went in again unto Sarah, and, behold, she conceived and bare him a son, and he was named Isaac; howsoever, he was but a puny child, and in no wise so strong and lusty as Ishmael, the son of Abraham and Hagar the Egyptian.

Wherefore Sarah was filled with envy toward Hagar, and she said unto Abraham: Cast out this bondwoman and her son; for the son of this bondwoman shall not be heir with my son, even with Isaac.

And the thing was grievous in Abraham's sight, for he was a man of a good heart, though weak.

But Jehovah said unto Abraham, Let it not be grievous in thy sight because of the lad, and because of thy bondwoman; in all that Sarah hath said unto thee hearken to her voice; for in Isaac shall thy seed be called.

And Abraham rose up early in the morning, and took bread and a bottle of water, and gave it unto Hagar, putting it on her shoulder, along with the child, and sent her away:

*Of Jeho-
vah's idea
of father-
hood*

and she departed, and wandered in the wilderness of Beersheba.

And the water was spent in the bottle, and she placed the child under one of the shrubs.

And she went and sat her down over against him a good way off, as it were a bowshot: for she said, Let me not see the death of my child. And she sat over against him, and lifted up her voice and wept.

And the Serpent appeared unto her, the same which had appeared unto Adam and Eve in the garden of Eden, and she followed the Serpent, until she beheld a well of water; and she went and filled the bottle with water, and gave the lad drink.

And they abode in the wilderness together with the Serpent; and the lad was taught by the Serpent, and he grew to manhood, strong and free, rejoicing in the waste places of the wilderness.

And his hand was against every man, and every man's hand was against him: therefore became he yet more strong and more free.

But Jehovah rejoiced, because of his power over Abraham; and he desired to show his power yet the more; wherefore he said unto him:

Abraham, take now thy son, thine only son,

34

Isaac, whom thou lovest, and get thee into the land of Moriah; and offer him there upon one of the mountains as a burnt offering unto me.

Then Abraham entreated Jehovah, and said unto him: All these years have I served thee, and sacrificed of my flocks upon thine altars, and impoverished me for thy sake; yea, and in obedience to thy commands, I cast out Ishmael, my beloved son, and I know not whether he be alive or dead. Lord, is it not enough?

And Jehovah said, It is not enough.

So Abraham rose up early in the morning, and laid the wood for the burnt offering upon Isaac his son, and they proceeded together.

And when they were come into the mountains of Moriah, Abraham built an altar there, and laid the wood in order, and bound Isaac his son, and laid him on the altar upon the wood;

And Abraham stretched forth his hand, and lifted up the knife above his son to slay him.

Then came the Serpent, stealing out from the rocks of the mountain, and the Serpent said unto Abraham, Thou fool!

And Abraham turned and said, Who speaketh unto me? Art thou one of the gods?

But the Serpent answered: I am not one of the gods; yet hearken unto my words, and, if

*Of Jeho-
vah's idea
of father-
hood*

the words be true in themselves, they could not be more true though a god spake them.

Lo, thou hast cast out thy son, Ishmael, and, had I not preserved him, he would have perished in the wilderness. And now thou art about to slay Isaac, thy remaining son.

Hopest thou to become the father of a nation? How art thou fit to be the father of a nation who art not fit to be the father of thy son?

And Abraham was smitten with remorse, and said, Yea, I have sinned, but it was because I feared Jehovah: for he will avenge himself upon me if I sacrifice not his sacrifice. Teach me, then, what I should do.

And the Serpent said, Sacrifice unto Jehovah yonder ram, and Jehovah will perceive not the deceit, for he will enjoy the savor of the ram. It is indeed a sin for thee to shed the innocent blood of the ram, yet is it a lesser sin. And I perceive thou art a man born to commit sin, either in one way or in another.

And Abraham lifted up his eyes, and beheld a ram caught in the thicket by his horns; and Abraham went, and took the ram, and offered him up for a sacrifice in the stead of his son.

And Jehovah enjoyed the sweet savor of

36

the offering and perceived not the deceit.

Therefore Jehovah praised Abraham, and said, Now shall I be called the God of Abraham unto all generations. But the Serpent, when he heard these words of Jehovah, smiled.

Of Jehovah's idea of fatherhood

CHAPTER IX

NOW all these things Satan said unto me, and many more.

Why Moses accepted Jehovah as his god

For Satan told me of Jacob, the son of Isaac, how that he deceived his father that was old and blind and tricked his elder brother Esau out of his father's blessing;

And of how that he fled away in terror of his brother Esau;

And of how that he gained much wealth in a far land by trickery and double-dealing;

And was in all things pleasing unto Jehovah, wherefore Jehovah named him Israel, signifying Soldier of God.

And Satan told me of how the children of this Israel went down into Egypt because of a famine and abode there.

And Satan said:

Now it came to pass that the Children of Israel, as they were called, did multiply exceedingly in the land.

And they worshipped the gods of the Egyptians; Ptah and Ra, Osiris, Isis, and Horus worshipped they; and these were indeed far

*Why
Moses
accepted
Jehovah as
his god*

wiser and greater gods than Jehovah. Wherefore Jehovah plotted in secret against the Children of Israel.

And they worshipped also the Serpent, under the name of Kneph. And when the Serpent perceived that the hearts of the Israelites yearned again toward their former land, he was moved with compassion, and sought to bring them out from among the Egyptians.

And he sent unto Pharaoh two magicians, of the names of Moses and Aaron, that they might persuade Pharaoh to let the people go: and Aaron cast down his rod before Pharaoh and before his servants, and it seemed as a serpent.

Then Pharaoh also called the wise men and the sorcerers: and these magicians of Egypt, they also did in like manner with their seeming enchantments.

For they cast down every man his rod, and they seemed as serpents: but Aaron's rod seemed to swallow up their rods.

Then Jehovah in secret plotted yet the more, and hardened Pharaoh's heart so that he would not let the people go.

And then the Serpent stirred the people to rise up by night and go out from the land; and

when the Egyptians followed them, they
turned and did battle with the Egyptians and
slew many of them, and escaped thence by a
ford, across one of the rivers which lead into
the Red Sea; and they came into the Wilderness, unto the land of Midian.

*Why
Moses
accepted
Jehovah as
his god*

And Jehovah beheld that they had escaped,
and he said unto himself, Now shall I win
them over unto me, for I needs must.

And Jehovah looked, and beheld Moses
walking in the land of Midian, and he came
down secretly and stole into a bush, saying,
Moses, Moses. And Moses said, Here am I.

And Jehovah said, Draw not nigh hither:
put off thy shoes from off thy feet, for the
place whereon thou standest is holy ground.

Behold, I have surely seen the affliction of
my people which were in Egypt, and I have
delivered them out of the hand of the Egyptians; and I shall bring them up out of this
wilderness unto the land of Canaan, which is
a goodly land, flowing with milk and honey.
Go now therefore, and proclaim my worship
unto them.

But Moses answered, Assuredly I had
thought that by the wisdom of the Serpent and
by the might of our own hands had we de-

*Why
Moses
accepted
Jehovah as
his god*

livered ourselves. And he called unto the Serpent and said, Art thou our god or art thou not?

And the Serpent said unto Moses: If ye will have gods, I am the best of them. Yet am I no god. Worship me if ye will, but if ye worship me not, I shall not therefore injure you. Worship whom ye will.

But Jehovah said, I, the Lord thy God am a jealous god, and if ye turn you from me, I shall destroy you utterly.

Then Moses thought it the part of wisdom to worship Jehovah.

And Moses said unto him, Behold, when I come unto the Children of Israel, and shall say unto them, A new god sendeth me unto you; and they shall say to me, What is his name? what shall I answer unto them?

And Jehovah said unto Moses, I am that I am: and he said, Thus shalt thou say unto the Children of Israel, I Am hath sent me unto you.

But Moses answered and said, Behold, now I have taken upon me to speak unto the Lord, which am but dust and ashes. Yet if I go unto the Children of Israel and say, The great god I Am hath sent me unto you, I shall surely be mocked of them.

And Jehovah answered, Then shalt thou say, instead, the Lord God of your fathers, the God of Abraham, the God of Isaac, and the God of Jacob, hath sent me unto you.

Why Moses accepted Jehovah as his god

And Moses answered, It is well. For when I announce unto them the god of their fathers, they will worship without question.

CHAPTER X

And Satan said:

Now the Children of Israel were in the wilderness, hard by the foot of Mount Sinai, the dwelling of Jehovah; so they deemed it wise to worship him.

Of Jehovah's difficulties with the Ten Commandments

And Jehovah said unto Moses, Come up to me into the mount, and I will give thee tables of stone, and a law and commandments which I have written; that thou mayest teach them.

And Moses went up into the mount, and a cloud covered the mount, and Moses went into the midst of the cloud, and abode with Jehovah forty days and forty nights. And Jehovah read unto Moses that which he had written upon the tables of stone. And Jehovah read aloud:

Thou shalt have no other gods before me.

And Moses said unto Jehovah, Let not the Lord be angry, and I will speak. For this commandment is not clear unto me: meaneth it that we may have other gods and worship them, provided that the first place in our worship be given to thee? Then Jehovah erased

45

Of Jeho-
vah's dif-
ficulties
with the
Ten Com-
mandments

the writing, and changed it, and he read:

Thou shalt have none other gods but me.

And he said, Is the commandment now clear? And Moses answered, Yea, O Lord, it is clear. And Jehovah continued, and read:

Thou shalt not make unto thee any graven image.

And Moses said unto Jehovah yet a second time, Let not the Lord be angry with his servant, and I will speak again. What harm cometh from the graven image? No man is so foolish as to mistake the image for the god himself, but it symbolizeth the god, and bringeth him near to the hearts of men. I pray thee, let our artificers make beautiful images, even as the artificers among the other peoples do.

And Jehovah answered, Yea, the artificers of the other peoples make beautiful images, but thy people knoweth not the way; and I will not have them to make images of me which be inferior to them that the other peoples make of their gods. Therefore, I say unto thee,

Thou shalt not make unto thee any graven image, nor the likeness of any thing that is in the heaven above or in the earth beneath or in the waters under the earth.

Then Moses spake unto Jehovah yet a third

46

time, saying, O let not the Lord be angry with his servant, who knoweth nothing; but I have heard the wise men of Egypt say that the earth is round and hangeth in space like to a great orange, so can there be no water under the earth.

*Of Jeho-
vah's dif-
ficulties
with the
Ten Com-
mandments*

And Jehovah answered and said: I created the earth and the water under the earth. Wast thou present at the creation to deny my words? Then Moses was abashed, and Jehovah continued:

Thou shalt not bow down to them nor worship them: for I, the Lord thy God am a jealous god, and visit the sins of the fathers upon the children unto the third generation of them that hate me.

Then Moses could not be silent, albeit that he was the meekest of men which were upon the face of the earth, but he spake yet once more and said, Lord, I am only a worm, but is this thy commandment, just? Methinketh it is not just, but unjust.

And Jehovah answered: What is justice but the will of the Lord thy God? Am I a man that thou shouldst accuse me of injustice? Moreover, thou hast broken into the reading of the law before that it was ended. For it endeth thus:

47

Of Jeho-
vah's dif-
ficulties
with the
Ten Com-
mandments

And show mercy unto thousands of them that love me and keep my commandments.

Then Moses was reconciled to this law, also, and Jehovah continued:

Thou shalt not take the name of the Lord thy God in vain; for the Lord will not hold him guiltless that taketh his name in vain.

And Moses spake yet again, O Lord, have pity upon me, but the meaning seemeth obscure. Meaneth it that a man shall not take any oath in a court of law, or that he shall not take an oath in behalf of a wrong cause; or applieth it to the light and vain words which men are wont to use in their times of anger? Surely, the latter were not worthy of thy note or of a special commandment.

But Jehovah answered, It meaneth that which it saith, and no more. And he continued:

Remember the sabbath day to keep it holy; six days shalt thou labor and do all that thou hast to do, but the seventh is the sabbath of the Lord thy God: in it thou shalt do no manner of work, thou, nor thy son, nor thy daughter, thy manservant, nor thy maidservant, nor thy cattle, nor the stranger that is within thy gates: for in six days the Lord made heaven and earth, the sea, and all that in them is, and rested the seventh day: wherefore the Lord blessed the seventh day and hallowed it.

And Moses said unto Jehovah, O Lord, have mercy upon me, for herein do I perceive matter for misunderstanding. Was the day on which thou didst begin to make the earth, the day of the Sun, which is called Sunday, or the day of the Moon, which is called Monday, or was it perchance yet some other day still? For how can man know which day to keep as the sabbath, save he know which day to consider as the first day?

And Jehovah began to be wroth, and he said unto Moses: Thou fool. Have I not said unto thee that the first day was that on which I did begin my labors, and that I rested upon the seventh day? Therefore thou shalt keep the seventh day holy as the sabbath, in which thou shalt not do any work, thou, nor thy son, nor thy daughter, nor the stranger that is within thy gates.

And Moses spake and said, O Lord, grant thy forgiveness unto me, but I perceive yet other matter of misunderstanding in this law. For that which is work unto one man is pleasure unto another, and how are they to be distinguished the one from the other?

But Jehovah answered: Thou speakest

Of Jehovah's difficulties with the Ten Commandments

49

*Of Jeho-
vah's dif-
ficulties
with the
Ten Com-
mandments*
many vain words. Work, it is always work, and pleasure, it is always pleasure. When I created the earth it was work, and when I rested on the seventh day it was pleasure. Let that suffice unto thee. And Jehovah continued:

Honor thy father and thy mother, that thy days may be long in the land which the Lord thy God giveth thee.

And Moses said unto Jehovah, O Lord, I am but dust and ashes, yet were it not well to add unto this, Honor also thy son and thy daughter that thy days may be long in the land?

But Jehovah answered, Wouldst thou render the children disobedient, and wouldst thou destroy the family? And Jehovah continued, and read aloud:

Thou shalt not kill.

And Moses said unto Jehovah, O Lord, I am a fool, yea, utterly a fool, but meanest thou this commandment? How is it possible that the Children of Israel should enter into the land of thy promise save they kill the inhabitants thereof?

Then Jehovah erased the writing, and changed it, and read:

Thou shalt do no murder.

50

And Jehovah said unto Moses, Art thou satisfied? And Moses answered, Yea, O Lord.

And Jehovah continued, and read:

Thou shalt not commit adultery.

And Moses said unto Jehovah, O Lord, forgive thy servant yet this once more, for I fear thine anger in this more than in aught else; therefore, forgive thy servant and tell him, What is adultery?

For if a woman erroneously supposeth her husband to be dead, and marrieth another, is that adultery? Or if a man is wedded unto a mad woman and leaveth her for another? Or if a man and a woman live together all their life long but without the law? Or if a man goeth in unto a harlot? Are all these adultery?

And Jehovah answered and said; Yea, they are all the same, and none shall be guiltless. For I say unto you, Adultery is adultery. And Jehovah continued, and read aloud:

Thou shalt not steal.

And Moses said unto Jehovah, O Lord, forgive thy servant and pardon him yet once again; but doth this law apply equally unto them that live in high places and unto the rich, that steal in secret, or doth it apply only to the poor, who steal openly?

And Jehovah answered and said: It is a

Of Jehovah's difficulties with the Ten Commandments

*Of Jeho-
vah's dif-
ficulties
with the
Ten Com-
mandments*

righteous law, and one which those whom I elect to position shall execute upon those within their power. And Jehovah continued:

Thou shalt not bear false witness against thy neighbor.

And Moses said unto Jehovah, O Lord, behold, my dullness passeth beyond belief, but meaneth this law what it seemeth to mean, that it is right to bear false witness on behalf of one's neighbor? Or is all false witnessing evil, and a thing to be condemned?

Then Jehovah began to be wroth once more, and made no answer, but he continued and read aloud:

Thou shalt not covet thy neighbor's house, thou shalt not covet thy neighbor's wife, nor his manservant, nor his maidservant, nor his ox, nor his ass, nor anything that is his.

And Moses said unto Jehovah, Lo, I am altogether sinful and unworthy to live; but puttest thou a man's wife in the same class with oxen and asses?

And Jehovah was very wroth, and said unto Moses: Yea, and I would put thee there also, for, truly, there thou belongest.

CHAPTER XI

AND Satan continued:

Then Jehovah said unto the Children of Israel, Get you up unto the land of Canaan, for I will bring you in unto the land, and I will give it you for a heritage: I am the Lord.

How Jehovah led the Children of Israel against the Amalekites

So the Children of Israel confided in the words of Jehovah, and got them up unto the land of Canaan, and prepared to do battle with the Amalekites, who held the way of that land.

And Jehovah said unto the Children of Israel, Hear, O Israel, ye approach this day unto battle against your enemies: let not your hearts faint, fear not, and do not tremble, neither be ye terrified because of them;

For the Lord your God is he that goeth with you, to fight for you against your enemies, to save.

And the Children of Israel went out to fight with the Amalekites; howsoever, they prevailed not against the Amalekites, but the Amalekites prevailed against them.

And the Children of Israel murmured

*How Jeho-
vah led the
Children of
Israel
against the
Amalekites*

against Jehovah, saying, He hath deceived us.
But Jehovah was not cast out of countenance,
for he answered and said, Nay, I will not
drive out the Amalekites at once before thee,
lest the land become desolate, and the beast
of the field multiply against thee:

By little and little I will drive them out
from before thee, until thou be increased and
inherit the land.

So the Children of Israel sent in spies to
search the land thoroughly, and they searched
it for forty days, and returned back safe unto
the Children of Israel.

And they brought up an evil report of the
land which they had searched, saying unto
the Children of Israel, The land through
which we have gone to search it, is a land
which eateth up the inhabitants thereof; and
all the people which we saw in it are men of a
great stature. We were in our own sight as
grasshoppers before them; and they are in
number like the sands upon the seashore.

Now when they heard this, the Children of
Israel murmured against Moses and Aaron:
and the whole congregation said unto them,
Would God that we had died in the land of
Egypt! or would God we had died in this
wilderness!

Now when Jehovah perceived from the report of the spies that the Amalekites were too strong for the Children of Israel, he spake unto Moses and Aaron, saying,

How Jehovah led the Children of Israel against the Amalekites

How long shall I bear with this evil congregation which murmur against me? I have heard the murmurings of the Children of Israel which they murmur against me;

Wherefore, say unto them, As truly as I live, saith the Lord, as ye have spoken in mine ears, so will I do to you.

Your carcasses shall fall in this wilderness, and your children shall wander in the wilderness forty years, until your carcasses be wasted in the wilderness.

After the number of the days in which ye searched the land, even forty days, each day for a year, shall ye bear your iniquities, and remain in this wilderness.

Then Moses said, Lord, I am no longer young. Shall I not see the land of thy promise, not even I?

And Jehovah answered, Yea, thou mayest ascend into the mountain of Abarim that overlooketh the land: thou mayest see it, but thou shalt not enter in;

For, when I delivered unto thee my commandments upon Mount Sinai, thou didst

How Jeho-vah led the Children of Israel against the Amalekites raise objections; yea, more than ten times didst thou raise witless objections. Thou, Moses, art stiff-necked, and I, the Lord thy God, do not forget.

CHAPTER XII

AND Satan said:

Now the Children of Israel abode in the wilderness, not forty years but thrice forty years, and they increased in numbers, and they increased in strength.

And they went up again against the Canaanites, and waged war with them for many years, yet had they little success against them.

And their first leader was Joshua, chosen by Jehovah, and a man of no account: under his leadership they conquered but the one city of Jericho, and it was taken by treachery.

For they sent up spies, which induced one Rahab a harlot, by means of bribes and a sum of money, to betray her own people, and unlock the gates of the city.

And because the city was taken through her, Rahab the harlot was much glorified among the Children of Israel, so that she dwelt with them until the end of her life, and pursued her calling with profit.

But thereafter came Jabin, King of Hazor, and oppressed the Israelites twenty years.

Of the kind of people chosen by Jehovah to be the leaders of Israel

57

Of the kind of people chosen by Jehovah to be the leaders of Israel

through the might of Sisera, the captain of his host. And at the end of the twenty years, Jehovah took courage to stir up one Jael, the wife of Heber the Kenite that was at peace with Jabin, to slay Sisera by treachery.

For she invited him into her tent when he was weary, and she bade him slumber in peace. But when that he slept she arose softly and took a nail of the tent and a hammer, and she stole up beside him and smote the nail into his temples, that he died.

And Jehovah said, Blessed among women shall Jael the wife of Heber the Kenite be, blessed shall she be among women.

Then Jehovah raised up judges, from time to time, to lead the Children of Israel against their enemies: first, Gideon, that led them out to one victory and then returned home, content, to beget children, for he had many wives, and begat threescore and ten sons upon them;

And after Gideon, Jair, that had thirty sons, and Ibzan, that had thirty sons and thirty daughters, and Abdon, that had thirty sons and forty reputed nephews.

Meanwhile, the Ammonites were strong in the land, and lorded it over the Israelites, for their judges did naught but beget sons and daughters.

CHAPTER XIII

Of Jeph-
thah
and his
daughter

AND Satan continued and said:

So, after a time, the Israelites came unto Jephthah, the son of a harlot, and besought him to save them from the Ammonites.

And Jephthah gathered the host of Israel together, and led them out against the Ammonites, and the battle was sore betwixt them.

And in the stress of the battle Jephthah vowed a vow unto Jehovah that, if the victory were his, he would sacrifice as a burnt offering to Jehovah whatsoever should first come forth from the doors of his house to meet him upon his return. And the victory was his.

And Jephthah returned to Mizpeh unto his house, and, behold, his daughter came joyously to meet him with timbrels and with dances; and she was his only child; beside her, he had neither son nor daughter.

And when Jephthah beheld her, he rent his clothes, and said, Alas, my daughter! Now hast thou brought me very low; for I have opened my mouth unto the Lord, and I cannot go back.

59

And she said unto him, My father, if thou hast opened thy mouth unto the Lord, do to me according to that which hath proceeded out of thy mouth.

And Jephthah said unto her, Yea; but first I will pray unto the Lord, and perchance he may remit my vow when he seeth that thou art my only child.

Then Jephthah prayed, saying, O Lord, behold, this my child hath neither sister nor brother; her mother is dead, and she is all that I have. Wilt thou take her away from me who have served thee these many years? Wilt thou not accept or name any ransom for her?

But Jehovah answered him not one word.

And she said unto her father, Let this thing be done for me: let me alone two months, that I may go up and down upon the mountains, and bewail my virginity, I and the maidens, my companions.

And he said, Go. And he sent her away for two months: and she went with the maidens, her companions, and bewailed her virginity upon the mountains.

And the daughter of Jephthah sang upon the mountains: Shine, Sun; let thy face be bright upon me; for I go down into the shadow.

Let me see the eyes of all the little stars upon me at night; for I go down into a darkness wherein is no star.

Let me clasp the earth and embrace her; soon shall she clasp me, but I shall not return her embraces.

Somewhere my husband waits for me, he that would have been my husband, but I cannot stay to meet him. Go elsewhere, husband; seek another bride; my lips will be too pale for thy kisses.

So sang the daughter of Jephthah upon the mountains; and it came to pass at the end of two months that she returned unto her father, who did with her according to his vow.

CHAPTER XIV

And Satan continued and said:

And thereafter came the Philistines, and lorded it over the Israelites many years. But at last Jehovah took courage to stir up against them one Samson, which was a man of great strength but a fool.

For he had been vowed from the day of his birth unto Jehovah as a Nazarite, upon whose head no razor might ever come; and Jehovah, that he might keep him in his service as a Nazarite, said unto him how that his strength abided in his hair and would depart from him if he were shaven.

And the silly Samson believed Jehovah.

Yet because of his strength he wrought much evil against the Philistines, and they might not prevail against him.

Therefore the chief men of the Philistines got them up unto Delilah that was the most beautiful of all their women, and they said unto her, Art thou willing to sacrifice thyself for thy people? And she said unto them, Yea.

And they said, Entice for us Samson, and

Of the hairy Samson and the beautiful Delilah

63

Of the hairy Samson and the beautiful Delilah

find out by what means we may prevail against him.

Then Delilah clothed herself in scarlet and gold, and dropped strange perfume upon her head, and put spices upon her breast; and she went up unto Samson, and her eyes flashed upon him, and he desired her.

But Delilah loathed him, for he was huge of body, and all his limbs were covered with a thick growth of hair; howsoever she remembered her people and let him take her unto him.

And thereafter by her woman's wit she learned what he deemed to be the secret of his strength; and when he fell asleep, she caused him to be shaven, and sent for the Philistines to come upon him.

And when Samson beheld the Philistines, he bellowed like a bull, and seized his sword to go against them; but Delilah said unto him, Look to thy hair, O Samson.

And when he saw what she had done, he dropped his sword, and stood still, bleating like a sheep that is newly shorn; and even like a sheep was he led away by them that took him.

Thus Delilah was released from the trial

which she had undergone for her people, and she said,

Lo, my shame is become mine honor, in loathing and disgust have I found my peace.

The worth of my body was little, and it is gone; the worth of my people is great, and it abideth.

And she bade the gods of the Philistines rejoice, singing,

Shout, O Baal, that rideth upon the heavens; dance, O Ashtoreth, that laugheth among the clouds.

The tower of Israel is fallen, is fallen, and the lion of Israel roareth no more.

Of the hairy Samson and the beautiful Delilah

CHAPTER XV

ALL these things Satan said unto me and much else.

For Satan told me of the reign of Saul, the servant of his people, and of how he was betrayed by his armor-bearer, David, he that went over to the Philistines and later became king of the Israelites and caused his captain Uriah the Hittite to be slain in order that he might enjoy Uriah's wife.

And Satan told me of Solomon, David's son, he that began his reign by the murder of Adonijah.

And Satan said:

Now when that Adonijah was slain, King Solomon fell upon his knees and prayed unto Jehovah: O Lord my God, thou hast made thy servant king instead of David my father; and I am but a little child: I know not how to go out or come in.

Give therefore to thy servant an understanding heart to judge betwixt that which is good and that which is evil.

And Jehovah was pleased with the de-

Of Jeho-
vah's gift
to Solomon

meanor of Solomon, and said unto him, I will do according to thy asking; behold, I give thee a wise and an understanding heart.

But despite these words of Jehovah, no one, not even a god, can give to another that which he doth not himself possess.

CHAPTER XVI

AND Satan said:

Then King Solomon built a great palace for himself, and a smaller temple for Jehovah; thirteen years did he build the palace of King Solomon, but the temple of Jehovah was finished in seven years.

And King Solomon took no heed of the design or proportion of the buildings, but he measured off their size, and he counted out the number of precious stones that went into their making, so that the size of his palace was greater and the precious stones therein were more numerous than in all other buildings upon the whole earth.

And King Solomon also built a summer palace for himself amid the cedar forest on the slopes of Mount Lebanon.

And King Solomon passed his hours in eating and drinking and making merry; in the palace of Jerusalem throughout the winter, and in the palace of Lebanon throughout the summer, eating and drinking and making merry.

69

Of the merry life of Solomon

Now Jehovah was wroth with King Solomon because that he had built his own palaces larger than the temple of Jehovah:

Wherefore Jehovah said unto him, Lo, thou hast built unto thyself great palaces, and unto me hast thou given a house no bigger than the house of a beaver; forasmuch as this is done of thee, I will surely rend the kingdom from thee.

Notwithstanding, in thy days I will not do it, for David thy father's sake: but I will rend it out of the hand of thy son.

Then King Solomon answered, Now blessed be the name of David my father. And he continued eating and drinking and making merry.

And King Solomon said, Behold, David my father had seven queens and ten concubines. An I not greater than my father in all else, in buildings and riches and power? Let me be greater in this thing also.

And he sent soldiers over the mountains, and sailors over the sea, to bring women unto him: from Arabia and the gates of Ophir, from India and China, brought they women of every color and from every clime.

And King Solomon increased until he had seven hundred wives and three hundred concubines. And then he ceased, for he could do no more.

Thereafter, in his old age, King Solomon wrote a book, and the text of the book was this:

Vanity of vanities, vanity of vanities, all is vanity.

One man among a thousand have I found; but a woman among all those have I not found.

Yea, women also are vanity and vexation of spirit.

And this was all the profit reaped by King Solomon from seven hundred wives and three hundred concubines.

CHAPTER XVII

Of the
later tribu-
lations of
Jehovah

AND Satan continued:

Now after the death of Solomon, it befell this time as Jehovah had said, for the kingdom was rent in twain, even into Israel in the north and little Judah in the south.

And for a time Jehovah abode in Israel. But Israel stood in dire peril, for there were mighty enemies abroad, Damascus and Assyria and Babylon.

And Jehovah stirred up certain men that went about the country calling themselves prophets, sowing dissension and causing trouble.

For whereas the wise men sought to unite the people, and said: Surely God should be the god of one's heart; then let one man worship one god, and another, another, if so they desire; but be we all as one man against our common enemies;

Whereas the wise men spake thus, the prophets said, Leave all to Jehovah; he is the Lord thy God, he alone can defend you.

And they went about reviling and cursing

73

*Of the
later tribu-
lations of
Jehovah*

all them of the people that worshipped not Jehovah, or that worshipped him not after their own manner.

Wherever they turned the prophets saw naught but sin, even where another would have seen no sin at all; they spent their days inveighing against it; nor would they listen to agreements with any other nation, nor took they any care to breed warriors to defend the people.

And Jehovah rejoiced, and said: Be not afraid. I will lift the yoke of your enemies from off your neck; and if they come upon you, I will stretch out my little finger, and they shall be as dust.

But in the midst of his boastings, the lion of Assyria came up against Israel.

And they that went out against the Assyrians were even as dust blown away by the tempest; they were driven before the Assyrians like sheep before the sandstorm, and the Assyrians followed and devoured them.

Then was Jehovah dreadfully afraid; he leaped from hill to hill like a grasshopper; from hill to hill he leaped until he got him away safely into Judah.

But in Judah he took heart again and said to the men of Judah:

74

Lo, the men of Israel forsook my worship, and I, even I, brought the Assyrians upon them to destroy them. Have ye not heard? Have ye not seen? As I am the Lord, I will do the same by you unless ye amend your ways.

Of the later tribulations of Jehovah

But ere long the Babylonians began to come like a swarm of locusts and eat up the earth. Naught might withstand them; neither Assyria nor Egypt; how then could little Judah withstand them?

And when Jehovah beheld the gods of Babylon, Bel, and Marduk, and Nebo, in the forefront of the battle, his heart again failed him, and he fled away, and hid himself, like a weasel that hideth himself in a hole.

But the men of Judah went gallantly against the Babylonians, and the chariots of the Babylonians rolled over them as a wave breaketh over the pebbles on the sea-shore; yea, the chariots crushed their bodies beneath them as one crusheth an ant-hill.

The arrows of the Babylonians fell upon them like a pestilence; the spears of the Babylonians smote them down like the plague.

The Babylonians burnt up the land of Judah like stubble before them; they entered into Jerusalem and rent the temple of Jeho-

*Of the
later tribu-
lations of
Jehovah*

vah as one rendeth a garment; and they led the people of Judah away captive as one leadeth a beast of burden, heavy-laden, into a far land.

CHAPTER XVIII

'AND Satan said:

Now it befell in due time that the headship of the earth passed from Babylon to Persia. And the remnants of the Jews lived at peace under the Persians.

And when Jehovah beheld that they were at peace, he crept back among them.

But the Jews learned many things of the Persians not to their own advantage.

For the Persians held that there be two gods, a god of light and a god of darkness, and that the god of light sendeth good upon men and the god of darkness sendeth evil.

Now when the Jews questioned Jehovah of this, Jehovah was at first wroth, and he answered, vehemently: Is there a god beside me? yea, there is no god; I know not any.

I am the first, and I am the last; and beside me there is no god. I am the Lord, and there is none else, there is no god beside me.

I form the light and create darkness: I

77

*What Je-
hovah
learned
from the
Persians*

make peace and create evil: I, the Lord, do all these things.

Howbeit, when Jehovah had reflected within himself, he perceived the merit in an evil god upon whom to place the blame for all that miscarries in the world, and Jehovah made haste to add,

True, there is none other god but me, yet is there also a devil, who goeth about through the world, seeking whom he may devour; and I alone can save you from the devil. Therefore worship ye me the more!

Now the Persians also taught that the god of light hath armies of angels to fight on his behalf, so the Jews questioned Jehovah of this also.

And Jehovah thought, Shall a miserable Persian god have armies of angels, and shall not I have angels? And he answered, Assuredly I have angels, yea, and archangels, cherubim and seraphim, thrones, dominations, principalities, and powers, all these have I beside me, under my command. Therefore worship ye me the more!

And the Persians also taught the doctrine of a future life, of a heaven wherein men be rewarded for their deeds on this earth, and of a hell wherein they be punished. And the

78

Jews questioned Jehovah of this, also.

And Jehovah said unto himself, Verily, the god of the Persians is a clever god; why had not I thought of this, myself, even I?

What Jehovah learned from the Persians

And Jehovah answered and said, Yea, there is a heaven of everlasting glory, wherein are Noah and Abraham, Moses, Rahab the harlot, Jael and David, and all them that have served me.

And there is also a hell of everlasting torment, wherein are Adam and Cain, Delilah, Saul, and all them that have hated me, even all the Canaanites, Moabites, Ammonites, Philistines and Egyptians, Assyrians and Babylonians, and many others, so that there be ten that suffer the agonies of hell to one that enjoyeth the rapture of heaven. Therefore worship ye me the more.

Thus was the last case of the Jews worse than the first, owing to that which they, and Jehovah, learned from the Persians.

For now at last, with the devil as his scapegoat, angels to protect him, and the gifts of eternal pleasure or pain in his hands, Jehovah lorded it over the Jews according to his heart's desire.

CHAPTER XIX

How Judas escaped from the Essenes

Now all these teachings of Satan I pondered in my heart. And my spirit waxed bitter against Jehovah because of the many evils which he had brought upon my people.

Thus it was that in my sixteenth year I stole away secretly from among the Essenes, and after much toil crossed the wilderness, and after three days came into the Valley of Jehoshaphat;

And I saw the grey walls of Jerusalem above me, but it was dusk, and I might not go up to them; so I searched, and found a cave in the hillside where I lay hidden all that night.

And in the morning I climbed the cliff above the Valley of Jehoshaphat, and entered into Jerusalem, and beheld the temple and all the things that be in this city.

CHAPTER XX

Of what Judas saw and learned in Antioch

Now at that time there was passing through Jerusalem, Apollonius, a Greek lord, of Antioch, very rich.

And one of his train, falling ill of the fever, must be left behind, and Apollonius needed another servant in his place.

Then I, being strong for my years, when I sought for the position, was chosen from among the others. For I desired to leave Jerusalem speedily, lest Barzillai should send after me and take me.

So I journeyed with the train of Apollonius northward, and came unto Antioch the Beautiful, the Crown of the East, and it was even in the harvest season when the fields were golden with the grain.

And when we were come within the white walls of Antioch, I found men more than I had supposed were upon the whole earth.

Men of every country were there, Greeks and Romans, Egyptians, Syrians, Persians, Jews of every tribe, and strangers from the far east.

Of what Judas saw and learned in Antioch

And beside the city, upon the river Orontes, rode the ships of all nations, and among them I saw the Roman galleys.

And within the city were temples to innumerable gods: to Zeus the omnipotent, and Apollo the golden; grey-eyed Athene, and laughing Aphrodite; Astarte, the queen of the heavens; the mighty Heracles; Adonis of the wounded thigh; Mithra, and Isis, and Baal, and many another.

And there was one temple, very beautiful, dedicated unto the Serpent, who is worshipped there by a secret name, which I may not reveal.

Such was the city in which I dwelt for ten years in the household of Apollonius. From being faithful in a few things, I came to be trusted with many things, and I rose to be the steward of his household.

And Apollonius was kind to me, and permitted me to study, so that I read the philosophers of Greece, and listened to her poets and teachers.

From them I learned both the beauty of truth, and the truth of beauty; and I beheld that the gods whom the Greeks had made were as much greater than Jehovah as the Greeks were greater than mine own people.

84

Howsoever, I was not allowed to forget that I was a Jew, and it came to pass in this wise.

Of what Judas saw and learned in Antioch

For Apollonius had a daughter of mine own age, and in the intervals of pleasure she looked often upon me, and in the intervals of work I talked with her.

And it came to pass that one day, when Apollonius was absent in the city, I knelt before her, and said unto her that I loved her; and she saying neither yea nor nay but seeking to withdraw, I caught hold upon her robe to stay her.

Then she laughed aloud, and Apollonius, who had privily returned, came into the chamber.

And when I said that I sought only to speak with the maid, he answered, Forgettest thou that thou art a servant and a Jew, that thou shouldst touch the robe of my daughter!

But when Apollonius advanced upon me with his sword, I struggled with him, and he was wounded, so that I came safe away.

Then I fled from Antioch into the mountains, and, since I dared not go back, turned my steps once more unto Judea.

85

CHAPTER XXI

AND my heart was bitter within me, and I cursed the pride of the rich, for I, that had doubled the wealth of Apollonius by my stewardship, was now cast out, for no crime, to die alone upon the mountains.

And it was the winter season: the snow fell and the wind raged, I saw birds drop down frozen, and the beasts were perishing.

Then I thought, Lo, many a fox hath no hole wherein to hide, and many a bird hath no nest, yet do they not despair: shall I, which am a man, be weaker than they?

So I took courage, and got me down into the lowlands, and my life was preserved. And I earned my bread by the sweat of my face, and went about from place to place.

But now that I was come amid the Jews once more, I felt that I was an alien among them. My spirit was homeless; I longed for I knew not what.

So that I envied even the beggars, saying unto myself, These are Jews, that worship the god of their fathers and are at one with their

How Judas first beheld Jesus

people: so if their bodies be cold, this warmeth their hearts.

But I, that left the Jews to live with the Gentiles, and am now cast out by the Gentiles to live with the Jews, what am I? Neither Jew nor Gentile.

Now toward the dusk of the evening, I found myself upon the road that leadeth into Nazareth.

Then was I aware of one walking before me, and I overtook him, and was about to enter into speech with him, when I heard the cry, Unclean, Unclean, and knew that a leper approached us.

So I stepped aside from the way, but that other remained in the midst of the way, until the leper was come up to him.

And even by the dim light of dusk I saw that the leper was in rags, and his body everywhere covered with sores, beyond the bandages. And even where I stood beside the way, the air stank from his sores.

Then was I ashamed that one in health should have sorrowed for himself, and my heart was filled with pity for the leper.

But when that other stood still in the way, the leper cursed him, and said, Thy peril be upon thyself. It is none of my doing. Knewest thou not that I am a leper, and unclean?

And the other answered, Yea, I knew, and even unto such am I sent.

Then the leper said unto him, Art thou a physician? Canst thou make me clean?

And the other answered in turn, I am a physician, but thy body I can not make clean, for that no man knoweth to do. But thy soul I can make clean, if thou wilt.

And the leper was amazed, and said, What meanest thou?

And the other, that spake of himself as a physician, said: Disease cometh from without, and whatsoever cometh from without defileth not a man, but that which cometh from within defileth him. Save thy thoughts are unclean, thou art not unclean. Thou knowest whether thou beest so, or no.

And the leper answered, Men have spat upon me, and cursed me, they thrust me out of mine house, they clothed me in rags, and before this day hath no man spoken kindly to me. And I have hated them all in my heart.

And the other said unto him, Hatest thou still, or believest thou that one man is thy brother?

And the leper answered, Stretch forth thy

How Judas first beheld Jesus

hand and touch my sores, and I will believe.

Then I beheld the physician reach forth his hand, and touch his sores; and the leper bowed his head, and they went on a space together; and when they parted, the leper said unto him, Master, thou hast made me clean.

Now when I beheld the act of the physician, my heart was touched, and I loved the man; howsoever, I followed not after him, but tarried beside the leper, for I saw that he had need of me.

For he said unto me, Yonder goeth one that loveth his fellows, and I, too, would now do good unto them. Tell me then what I should do. Then I was silent, but he read my thoughts.

Wherefore he said, Thou art right. Give me thy dagger for but a moment. (For I carried at my waist the Syrian dagger that I had worn when I was the steward of Apollonius).

And when I had given him the dagger, he smote himself to the heart therewith.

Then I bore his body far away into the open fields, and covered it with earth, and bathed myself in a spring beside the way.

And at night I entered into Nazareth, and my spirit rejoiced because of the words of the physician and the deed of the leper.

CHAPTER XXII

THEN the next day I sought for the physician throughout the city, and behold, I found him teaching in the synagogue.

And when I spake with them that stood without, I learned that his name was Jesus, a carpenter's son of Nazareth, that had rebelled against his parents when he was twelve years old, and left them; and had travelled far into the East to be taught by the Magi and the Chaldæans, and by the wise men that dwell even to the east of the Chaldæans.

And now is he returned, they said, and seeketh to instruct us, who knew him when he was a puling infant in his mother's arms.

Then I went into the synagogue, and the first words which I heard Jesus say in the synagogue were these:

Ye worship ye know not what: for not one among you hath found his god in his heart, but ye have taken your god from books;

And ye think to win his favor by prayers and sacrifices, and ye think that the syna-

How Jesus taught in the synagogue at Nazareth

gogues and the temple at Jerusalem alone are holy.

But the hour cometh and now is, when the true worshippers shall worship in spirit and in truth.

God is Spirit, and they that worship him must worship in spirit and in truth.

Needeth one to go into a temple to worship him? The whole earth is his temple.

Wherever there are two, they are not without God, and wherever there is one alone, I say, God is with him. Raise the stone, and there thou shalt find him; cleave the wood, and there is he.

In the thunder ye shall hear the voice of his strength; go out beneath the stars, and ye shall feel his peace.

Take of his strength and his peace, and build in your midst the kingdom of heaven.

After these words he was silent.

But there were Pharisees and scribes in the synagogue that liked not the teaching, and they murmured, and said:

If the kingdom is in heaven, how can we build it in our midst? And who are they that should draw us unto this kingdom? Speak the law and the prophets thereof?

Jesus said unto them, Ye ask who are those

that draw us to the kingdom, and if the kingdom be in heaven?

How Jesus taught in the synagogue at Nazareth

The fowls of the air, and all beasts that are upon the earth, and the fishes of the sea, these are they which draw you.

And the kingdom of heaven is within you: and whosoever shall know himself shall find it. Strive therefore to know yourselves, and ye shall be aware that ye are the sons of the Almighty Father: ye shall know that ye are in the city of God, and ye are the city.

Thus he spake, and I said unto myself, Whence hath this man such wisdom? From the East? For he speaketh better than the philosophers of the Greeks, and even with more power. But then I thought, Wisdom speaketh with one voice wherever she speaketh at all.

But the Pharisees would not understand, for they said, If the kingdom of God shall come upon the earth, tell us at what time or what season it cometh.

Jesus answered, The kingdom of God cometh not with observation: neither shall they say, Lo here, or, lo there! for, behold, the kingdom of God is within you.

Then why even of yourselves judge ye not what is right, instead of searching the Scriptures?

How Jesus taught in the synagogue at Nazareth

But they murmured against him, and said, Is not this the carpenter's son? is not his mother called Mary? and his brethren, James, and Joses, and Simon, and Judas?

Whence then doth he presume in this fashion?

Jesus said unto them, A prophet is not without honor save in his own country.

Then were they but the more incensed, and they said, Makest thou thyself the equal of the prophets? By what authority comest thou to teach unto us strange doctrine? For neither the prophets nor the patriarchs spake of God as ye have spoken.

Jesus answered unto them, It seems I speak in a language that ye cannot understand. But now will I speak unto you even in your own language.

Think ye that he of whom I speak is the God of Abraham, and the God of Isaac, and the God of Jacob? I tell you, Nay, God is not the god of the dead but of the living.

Then there began an uproar among the Pharisees, but Jesus continued:

I say unto you that many shall come from the east and the west, and shall sit down in the kingdom, but the children of the kingdom shall be cast into outer darkness;

For I tell you of a truth many widows were in Israel in the days of Elias, when the heaven was shut up three years and six months, when great famine was throughout all the land;

How Jesus taught in the synagogue at Nazareth

But unto none of them was Elias sent, save unto Sarepta, a city of Sidon, unto a woman that was a widow.

And many lepers were in Israel in the time of Eliseus the prophet; and none of them was cleansed, saving Naaman the Syrian.

And when he had spoken these words, Jesus was silent. And my heart rejoiced, for I beheld how he had turned their own fables against them.

But all they in the synagogue were filled with wrath, and rose up, and thrust him out of the synagogue, and even out of the city.

CHAPTER XXIII

Now when Jesus was thrust out, I tarried behind and mingled with the people; and in the midst of the people stood a man heavy of stature and dull of visage.

And all the people reproached him, saying, Joseph, why permittest thou thy son thus to blaspheme?

And the man was vexed, and turned him unto his wife, and said, Mary, this is thine affair. Was he not ever thy son rather than mine? Did I not leave him solely unto thy direction when he was yet a child and I found I could do naught with him? And did I not tell thee oft that he would go astray?

And the woman wept, saying, I did not think it would come to this.

But their sons, who were four, spake loudly, Lo, our brother is become mad, and is beside himself. We will go out and take him and lay hold on him.

And Mary said, I will go with you that ye harm him not. But his father said, From this day forth my son hath no portion in me, for

Why Judas became a follower of Jesus

Why Judas became a follower of Jesus

he hath brought shame upon me; let them take him, and bring him back into the city in chains.

Then I rose up and rebuked them all to their face, saying, What is this? First ye cast the man out, and now ye would bring him back by force. Behold, ye are fools indeed.

But all the people turned and fell upon me, and rent my clothes, crying, We will teach thee whether we be fools or no.

Howbeit I gat free from them at the last, and sped away quickly before them out of the city; and upon the road to Capernaum I overtook Jesus, where he tarried with a few that followed him.

And I came and stood before him, all bloody, crying out, Behold, thy parents and thy brethren seek for thee to take thee. And this have they done unto me for that I rebuked them.

Then Jesus was silent for a little space, and his face was sad. But those about him spake loudly, saying, Thou must return. For the Scripture saith, Honor thy father and thy mother; if a son be disobedient unto his parents let him be stoned.

But unto them Jesus answered slowly, Who is my father or my mother? And he pointed

98

with his finger toward me, and said, Behold my father and mother! For whosoever is one in spirit with me, the same is my brother and sister and mother.

Why Judas become a follower of Jesus

Then the others were offended in him, and said, Comest thou to destroy the family?

But Jesus answered unto them, Nay, think ye that I am come to bring war upon the earth? I come not to bring a sword, but peace.

Wheresoever there is union of spirit, there is a family, indeed! And this cometh sometimes among those joined of nature, but it is a rarity.

Howsoever, not I, but God saith this, who hath destroyed many families.

For a man's foes be usually of his own household.

Then all those which followed him were indignant, and left him, and returned back into the city.

And Jesus and I journeyed on alone together.

And Jesus said unto me, How is it that thou also hast not left me, and turned back?

I answered unto him, Master, because I know from mine own life that all that thou sayest is true.

And I told him of Barzillai my father, and

Why Judas became a follower of Jesus

of my deeds from the day that I was first brought into the wilderness; and of how I hated Jehovah, the god of the Jews, that had made my people a hateful people, and yet had fettered me unto them by unbreakable fetters.

And I said, Let me follow thee, for I believe that the god whom thou proclaimest will destroy Jehovah.

But Jesus answered unto me, Judas, thou hatest well. Canst thou love well, also?

And I answered, Master, I can love thee, even unto death. But meanest thou that I must love all men?

Then Jesus said unto me, Thou must love the God in all men. To the end that he be realized in all men, some must be utterly destroyed.

Therefore I say unto thee, Love the God in men, and strive to thy uttermost that the time may come when he shall be realized in all men.

CHAPTER XXIV

AFTER, as we went upon the way together, I said unto Jesus, Art thou a physician of men's souls only, or of their bodies, also?

And Jesus answered unto me, How could I be a physician of the soul and not of the body, also? For the soul and the body are one. Do not the ills of the body make ill the soul likewise? And if the soul is ill, doth not the body suffer? For I say unto thee, the soul is the excellence of the body. Therefore let us give our lives that men may have better bodies and better souls.

For the ills of life are three: sickness, and poverty, and sin; and these three are one evil.

For when the body is sick, the hands are weak and cannot labor, and poverty stealeth on apace; and when the belly is empty and the tongue parched, then one stoopeth to sin.

But sin is folly and ill judgment, making one's poverty the worse; and as one's poverty groweth worse, he hath the less with which to fend off sickness.

Of the sayings of Jesus unto Judas

*Of the
sayings of
Jesus unto
Judas*

Therefore I say unto thee that sickness leadeth to poverty, and poverty to sin, and sin leadeth to poverty, and poverty to sickness, and the three are one evil.

And I am come to make war upon the three forms of the one evil.

Then I said, Yea, Master, but the rich: do they no sin?

Jesus answered unto me, The rich do far worse, they make others to sin.

Therefore said I unto thee, To the end that God be realized in all men, some must be utterly destroyed.

But the rich will not destroy themselves: then is my message not to the rich but to the poor.

Let us therefore help the poor against sickness and against sin, to the end that they become strong to overcome the rich, and do away with the poverty that leadeth to sickness and to sin.

For I say unto thee, The lack of money is the root of all evil.

Then because of these sayings of Jesus, I went with him yet the more willingly.

And we passed throughout all Galilee, healing many of them that were diseased, and spreading the gospel of Jesus to the poor.

THE FRIEND OF JESUS

Paralytics which were brought to him recovered the strength of their limbs, and threw away their crutches, and danced for joy;

And those whom the Greeks call epileptics, but whom the superstitious affirm to be possessed of devils, were healed of their madness by him.

And he was received into the houses of the poor, and made welcome; he brought with him health and gladness.

And I loved the man more and more; for virtue went out of him; and he was like unto no other man whom I have ever known.

CHAPTER XXV

HE was a buckler of strength unto the weak, and unto the poor he was a tower of joy.

They were like oxen beneath the yoke, they lay like worms upon the ground; he made them to run like young colts in the pasture, he sent their spirits on errands through the sky.

He lifted them up with the right hand of fellowship; with the right hand of fellowship he rescued their souls.

His touch upon the sick was soft as the summer waves of Galilee; calm as the waters by Magdala were the words of comfort that he spake; and deep as the depths by Capernaum was the depth of his love for men.

The snows of Lebanon were not whiter than his soul; and as the dew of Hermon was the coolness of his hands.

He took men into his heart as into a cup; he wiped away their tears with a word.

Such was Jesus in the days when first I knew him, surpassing the nightingale in sweetness, surpassing the lion in strength.

Other men might speak the same words,

*Judas' tes-
timony of
Jesus*

but they were no longer the same. Because Jesus was Jesus and no other, but to look upon him made men strong in themselves.

I, Judas, that later betrayed him, bear this witness of him.

CHAPTER XXVI

NOW upon a certain day we passed through a city wherein dwelt one Levi, a publican, that had known Jesus aforetime. And Levi made him a feast in his own house: and there was a great company of publicans and of others that sat down with us.

How Jesus ate with publicans and sinners

But the scribes and Pharisees murmured against us, saying, Why do ye eat with publicans and sinners?

And when Jesus heard it, he went out, and said unto them, They that deem themselves whole send not for the physician, but they that are sick send for him: nor came I to call the righteous, but sinners, to repentance;

For it is conceivable that these sinners should attain unto righteousness, but it is not conceivable that ye, who are so righteous, should ever attain unto sin.

Then were they perplexed, and knew not what he meant, wherefore he spake unto them a parable, saying, Of a truth there be dead things and living things.

A stone is dead and moveth not itself, but

How Jesus ate with publicans and sinners a fish is living and moveth. Therefore even the crab, which goeth backward, moveth more than doth a stone.

But ye are like the stone that moveth not at all. For if ye do no evil, ye think that ye have done somewhat, yet have ye done nothing at all.

Verily, verily, the man that doeth neither good nor evil is worse than he that doeth evil.

Therefore I say unto you that the publicans and the harlots go into the kingdom of God before you.

CHAPTER XXVII

THEN were the Pharisees greatly incensed, and one of them stood forth, and said, Behold, it is rumored that thou dost not observe the Law of Moses to fast upon the appointed days. Tell us whether this be the truth.

How Jesus denied the Law of Moses

Jesus answered unto him, It is the truth.

Then said the Pharisees, How darest thou set thyself up as a teacher among us when thou dost not even observe the Law?

And Jesus answered unto them again by a parable, saying, No man putteth new wine into old bottles; else the new wine will burst the bottles, and be spilled, and the bottles shall perish.

But new wine must be put into new bottles; and both are preserved.

No man, also, having drunk old wine straightway desireth new: for he saith, The old is better.

Then one of them that stood by, not a Pharisee, said unto Jesus, What is this new wine of which thou speakest? Hast thou a

*How Jesus
denied the
Law of
Moses*
new commandment which supersedeth the commandments of Moses?

Jesus answered unto him, The one commandment is that thou shalt have no commandments.

Howbeit, if thy soul yearneth for commandments, hearken unto me: Learn to know thyself; this is the first and great commandment.

And the second is like unto it: Learn to know thy neighbor as thyself.

These two commandments destroy all the law and the prophets.

For when a man learneth to know himself, he needeth no other prophet. For he knoweth his own desires, and he learneth whether they be gainful or harmful; and he learneth that his true desire may not be satisfied save the desire of all be satisfied: for every man is but part of a living whole.

Shall a man's finger lift itself against his other members, or a man's foot go to war against his hand?

Learn what thou art, and thou wilt learn to love thy neighbor as thyself, for thou livest in him even as in thyself.

This I say unto thee not for the sake of thy neighbor but for thine own sake. For love benefiteth not him that is loved but him that loveth.

How Jesus denied the Law of Moses

Howbeit, if thou wouldst benefit thy neighbor, learn to know him as thyself: for if thou knowest him not, thou canst not benefit him, though thou lovest fourfold.

But if thou knowest thyself and thy neighbor, thou knowest the living God. Pray, therefore, that this come to pass.

But when ye pray, use not vain repetitions, entreating many times, Lord, have mercy upon us, or Good Lord, deliver us;

Nor, when ye pray, be ye as beggars, grovelling upon the earth, and asking for wealth, or rain for your crops, or worldly glory; ask only for those things which the Lord within you may grant.

After this manner, therefore, pray ye:

Our Father, which art within us, hallowed be thy name. Thy kingdom come, thy will be done upon the earth. Help us this day to earn our daily bread. May we forgive our own sins nor bear them too bitterly in our hearts, and may we forgive those who sin against us. Lead us into temptation, for without temptation is no virtue possible, yet save us from such evil as destroyeth the soul. Amen.

CHAPTER XXVIII

THEN behold, from out of the crowd advanced a young man, clothed in purple and fine linen, and he said unto Jesus, Good Master, what very good thing shall I do, that I may have eternal life?

How Jesus preached against the rich

And Jesus said unto him, Why callest thou me good? there is none good but one, that is, God: but if thou wilt enter into life keep the commandments.

He saith unto him, Which? For of the commandments of Moses, thou knowest that some be foolishness.

Jesus answered, The other commandments which I have but now uttered in thy hearing.

The young man saith unto him, Those things have I kept from my youth up. No man better than I knoweth himself or his neighbor; witness my riches thereto. But what lack I yet? for I deem not myself to be perfect.

Jesus said unto him, If thou wilt be perfect, Go and sell that thou hast, and give to the poor.

*How Jesus
preached
against the
rich*

But when the young man heard that saying he went away sorrowful: for he had great possessions.

Then said Jesus unto them that remained, Verily, I say unto you, It is easier for a camel to go through the eye of a needle, than for a rich man to enter into the kingdom of heaven.

And they questioned him, Why so? Meanest thou that all men should become beggars?

Jesus answered unto them, Nay, I am no beggar, neither is Judas of Kerioth here with me: for I am both a carpenter and a physician, and he is strong with his hands to work in the fields.

What a man earneth, either with his hands or his wits, that is his wages; let him receive them. But whatsoever more he obtaineth is not rightfully his.

And whosoever is content with his wealth while so much as one man in the whole land shall lack bread, the same enters not into the kingdom of heaven.

Therefore I say unto you, upon the face of the whole earth there is not seen one good rich man. For if good, he would not consent to be rich and at ease while his brethren are suffering and poor.

Though a rich man oft hath the words of brotherhood upon his lips, yet hath he no brotherhood in his heart, or he would no longer remain rich.

How Jesus preached against the rich

Now when he had spoken those words, Jesus and I passed out from among them.

But from that day all the rich banded together with the scribes and Pharisees against us; and thenceforth there was no city in Galilee into which we were able to be received.

For when Jesus cured men of their physical ills, they rejoiced; but when he sought to cure them of spiritual ills, they reviled and persecuted him.

Wherefore we went down to the Sea of Galilee, and took ship, and crossed to the other side; and the place where Jesus was born saw him no more.

CHAPTER XXIX

YET through the deeds of healing that Jesus had wrought, his fame was gone out into all the country-side, and even beyond Jordan.

How it was rumored that Jesus had raised one from the dead

So when we took ship, and crossed the Sea of Galilee, and were come into the country of the Gadarenes, even as we entered into the city of Gadara, one met us, crying,

Master, my daughter lieth at the point of death. Wilt thou not come and heal her?

But when we went with the man unto his house, certain ones came out, saying, Trouble not the physician, for thy daughter is even now dead.

Then Jesus answered unto them, Let me behold the damsel. And when he was entered in and beheld the damsel, he saw that she lay in a trance.

Wherefore he said unto them, The damsel is not dead but sleepeth. But they laughed him to scorn.

Then Jesus bent over the damsel, and took her hand, and said unto her, *Talitha cumi,*

117

*How it was
rumored
that Jesus
had raised
one from
the dead*
which is, being interpreted, Damsel, I say unto thee, arise.

And the damsel arose from her trance, and lived.

Now when this was noised abroad, a foolish report went about that Jesus had raised one from the dead.

And, because of this, we were now thronged with people by day and by night, so that we had not one hour unto ourselves.

And some among them came to be healed, and many to gape and marvel, and a few to hear the words of life.

Now of these, some came unto Jesus, and said, Master, permit us to follow thee and become thy disciples.

But Jesus answered unto them, Think ye that I seek to found a sect, after the manner of others? I teach the word of the living God.

Were I to found a sect, the word would become lifeless: for the letter killeth, but the spirit maketh alive.

Then were they but the more insistent, saying, Let us follow thee, and partake of the spirit, and give unto others.

And Jesus was moved by their entreaties,

118

and withdrew a little apart, and communed with himself.

And he said unto me: Judas, what thinkest thou? Behold, I am but one, and the life of one is frail as the reed, and passing as the wind.

Shall I not take of these that they may spread the gospel after I am gone?

Now though I liked it not, because they seemed to me in the main witless men, nevertheless I held my peace.

And he took eleven; and of them Thomas was the best, for he had an enquiring mind; and Simon Peter and John, though ignorant, were men of some parts; but the rest were naught.

How it was rumored that Jesus had raised one from the dead

CHAPTER XXX

CHAPTER XXX

Now early in the morning Jesus went out into the city, and entered into the synagogue, and all the people came unto him; and he sat down, and taught them.

And the scribes and Pharisees brought unto him a woman taken in adultery; and when they had set her in the midst, they said unto him, Master, this woman was taken in adultery.

Now Moses in the Law commanded us that such should be stoned: but what sayest thou?

This they said, tempting him, that they might have new matter whereof to accuse him. But Jesus stooped down, and with his finger wrote on the ground, as though he heard them not.

So when they continued asking him, he lifted up himself, and questioned them: Doth the woman confess that she hath sinned? They answered, Yea. Then he said unto them: He that is without sin among you, let him first cast a stone at her. And again he stooped down, and wrote on the ground.

Of Jesus and the woman taken in adultery

And they which heard it, being convicted by their own conscience, went out one by one, beginning at the eldest even unto the last: and Jesus was left alone, and the woman standing in the midst.

When Jesus had lifted up himself, and saw none but the woman, he said unto her, Woman, where are those thine accusers? hath no man condemned thee?

She answered, No man, Master. And Jesus said unto her, Neither do I condemn thee: go, and sin no more.

And the woman departed, and returned unto him that had been her husband, and he received her not; and from there she went unto her own people in another city, and they cast her out into the street with curses.

And so the woman became a harlot.

All this we learned from her own mouth later in the city of Joppa.

But better had it been that Jesus had never met with that woman, either then or at any other time! For she was destined to do much harm unto him in the latter days.

Now the name of the woman was Mary of Magdala.

CHAPTER XXXI

THEN as we journeyed upon our way, Thomas said unto Jesus, Master, how knowest thou that the woman sinned? For perchance her husband hated and ill-used her, and there was no bond between them save the bond of the law.

Of a discourse upon sexual matters

But Jesus turned unto the other disciples, and said, Why think ye that the woman sinned? And they all with one accord made answer, Because she brake the Law of Moses.

Jesus said unto them, Lo, ye have heard that it was said by one of old time, Thou shalt not commit adultery.

But I say unto you, That whosoever looketh on a woman to lust after her hath committed adultery with her already in his heart.

Thomas said unto him, Then hath every man committed adultery many times.

Jesus answered unto him, Even so. And he that committeth adultery in his heart is no better than he that committeth it in act; nay, it may be that he only lacketh the courage, and is then the worser of the two.

Judge, therefore, not according to the appearance, but judge righteous judgment.

Then the other disciples were satisfied, but Thomas questioned yet again, In what did the woman sin?

Jesus said unto him, Heard ye not that she did confess that she had sinned?

For as long as the prince of darkness ruleth in this world, that woman sinneth against herself that accepteth the law of man in her heart and abideth not by it.

Howbeit, when the kingdom of heaven is established, this will be no longer so.

For in the kingdom of heaven they will neither marry nor be given in marriage.

Neither will the wife hang like a millstone about the neck of the husband, nor the husband lie like a weight of iron upon the bosom of the wife, nor will little children be branded with scars of shame from the day of their birth.

Then, when the disciples heard all these words, their eyes glistened, and they said, When will the kingdom of heaven be established?

But Jesus looked upon them sorrowfully,

and said, When ye shall be naked, and yet not ashamed.

And their faces became sad, and they pulled their robes closely about them, and said, Alas, of a truth this is not for us.

Of a discourse upon sexual matters

CHAPTER XXXII

NOW upon another day there were brought
unto Jesus little children that he should put
his hands upon them in blessing: and the disciples rebuked them.

But Jesus said, Suffer the little children,
and forbid them not, to come unto me: for
of such is the kingdom of heaven.

And while he blessed them, and, after, was
talking with them playfully, the disciples
stood apart, and asked among themselves
what he meant by those words.

And Simon Peter, who was a credulous
man by nature, said unto the rest, He meaneth
that we should receive his words without question, whatsoever they may be, even as little
children receive the words of their parents.

For we live by faith and not by knowledge.

But Thomas said unto him, Simon, Simon,
it is plain to be seen that thou hast had no
children of thine own. Else hadst thou heard
them questioning from morn till eve of
everything that lieth in the heavens above or

127

the earth beneath or the waters under the earth.

Then said John unto them, Nay, Jesus meaneth that we should forget ourselves utterly, and live in peace, as little children do, and have all things in common.

But Thomas said yet again, John, it is plain that thou also hast had no children of thine own. Else hadst thou heard them quarreling from dawn till sunset, and saying, This is not thine but mine; thou hast no right to it, for it is mine.

Then they all turned unto Thomas, and said, What thinkest thou that he meant, since thou art so wise to instruct us? But Thomas was speechless. For he was a man better at asking questions than at answering them.

And I could bear with their folly no longer, but said unto them:

Behold, when ye shall look upon the stars of heaven as though ye had never witnessed them before, and the rising of the moon shall seem a miracle unto you;

When the sunlight glancing upon a puddle shall move your hearts to song; when your whole soul shall cling about a single almond blossom in the spring-time;

When one breath of air from the snow

fields shall fill your body from the crown of your head to the soles of your feet; and when ye shall behold something new in every man whom ye pass by, and in every worm that ye tread into the ground;

Then, and not until then, will ye become as little children.

But the disciples said, Judas, also, speaketh things hard to understand, and they returned to their babbling among themselves.

Of a discourse upon children

CHAPTER XXXIII

Now after that we had abode many days in that country by the further shores of the Sea of Galilee, and Jesus had gained many followers among the poor of that country, I urged upon him that we should go up to Jerusalem.

Of a discourse upon laws and lawyers

For, fool that I was, I yearned to meet the powers of Jehovah in their stronghold, and overcome them.

So we took ship, and sailed unto the southernmost point of the Sea of Galilee, and from thence Jesus steadfastly set his face to go to Jerusalem.

And he sent messengers before his face: and they went, and entered into a village of the Samaritans to make ready for him.

And they did not receive him, because his face was as though he would go to Jerusalem.

And when his disciples, James and John, saw this, they said, Master, wilt thou that we command fire to come down from heaven, and consume them, even as Elias did?

(For this is one of the foolish tales which

Of a dis-
course upon
laws and
lawyers

are current among the Jews concerning Elias.)

But Jesus turned, and rebuked them, and said, Ye know not what manner of spirit ye are of, that ye deem ye have such power.

Nor is the Son of Man come to destroy men's lives, but to save them. And we went to another village.

And the people of the village made us welcome, and said unto Jesus, Master, we know that thou art true, and teachest the way of God in truth, neither carest thou for any man: for thou art no respecter of persons.

Tell us, therefore, what thinkest thou? Is it lawful to give tribute unto Caesar, or not?

But Jesus said unto them, Shew me the tribute money. And they brought unto him a penny.

And he saith unto them, Whose is this image and superscription?

They say unto him, Caesar's. Then saith he unto them, Render therefore unto Caesar the things which are Caesar's; and unto God the things that are God's.

But the more zealous among them made answer, Because Caesar hath placed his image upon our money, doth that make the law of tribute just?

Behold, not only this law, but many other laws of the Romans be unjust.

Of a discourse upon laws and lawyers

Jesus answered, Yea, and the laws of your forefathers among you were unjust. And the laws of them that come after you will be unjust. For if by chance a just law is recorded, yet by the manner of its enforcement is it made unjust.

Therefore whether ye be in the right, or whether ye be in the wrong, avoid all manner of dealing with the law.

Otherwise will ye be devoured by the state, or, if ye escape devouring by the state, ye will be devoured by the lawyers.

For the state devoureth you whole, and the lawyers devour you piecemeal, but in either lot ye are well and fully devoured.

Then said I unto Jesus, Master, if we give over this world unto Caesar, what is left unto God?

Were it not better to build a state wherein the evils of which thou speakest should not come to pass?

But Jesus looked round upon the disciples, and then said unto me, Thinkest thou that with such men as these I could build a state?

Nay, the building of such a state is a task

*Of a dis-
course upon
laws and
lawyers*

beyond my strength, which I leave to them that come after me.

Mine it is but to sow the seed of the kingdom of heaven, and when the seed shall have sprung up and borne fruit, then may the state be builded.

But years and perchance hundreds of years and perchance thousands of years must pass ere that time be come.

CHAPTER XXXIV

AND we departed from the borders of Samaria, and came into the land of Judea, even unto Jerusalem.

And when Jesus was come into Jerusalem, many were moved, saying, Who is this? And others answered, This is Jesus, the prophet of Nazareth of Galilee.

And he went into the temple, and cast out all them that sold and bought in the temple, and overthrew the tables of the money-changers, and the seats of them that sold doves.

And he said unto them, It is written, My house shall be called the house of prayer; but ye have made it a den of thieves.

For behold, when the people come up to sacrifice, they must first buy the goods of the sacrifice from you, and at the price ye name;

Wherefore ye are thieves, and robbers of the people.

For ye make them to sacrifice thrice, once to you, and once unto the priests, and once unto Jehovah.

135

How Jesus cast the money-changers out of the temple

Now when the chief priests saw the things that Jesus did, they were sore displeased;

For they knew in their hearts that they also, that partook of the things sacrificed, were robbers of the people;

And that Jehovah, who commanded the sacrifice, was the greatest robber of them all.

CHAPTER XXXV

BUT many of the people said, Of a truth this is the Prophet.

Others said, This is the Christ. But some said, Shall Christ come out of Galilee?

Hath not the Scripture said that Christ cometh of the seed of David, and out of the town of Bethlehem where David was?

So there was a division of the people because of him. And rumors went about among them concerning him, some true, but more of them untrue.

And at night came Peter and John and James, who had been all day with the people, and Peter said unto Jesus,

Strange things be reported in this Jerusalem concerning thee and thy mother. And I know not whether to believe or not to believe. Jesus said unto him, Say on.

And Peter said unto him, Behold, they say that an angel appeared unto Mary thy mother, and prophesied that she should bear a son without knowing man; and that thou wast

137

*Of what
Jesus spake
concerning
his birth*

conceived not of Joseph but of God himself in the likeness of the Holy Ghost.

Then was Jesus indignant, and said, Would they make of my mother a harlot?

And would they make of God a seducer of women?

But I said unto him, Master, be not indignant; the story cometh, as I think, from the Greeks that be among the people in Jerusalem, for they have many such tales touching their own gods.

And Jesus answered, Yea, and so have the men of the great East, touching the Buddha, as they name their Messiah. But I thought not that such tales arose during one's own lifetime.

Then Peter said unto him; They mean no harm to thy mother; rather do they say that she is honored above all women because that she is yet a virgin.

But Jesus answered. Wherefore should a virgin be honored above other women? For I say unto you that until a woman hath known a man, she hath not yet begun to be a woman. And I say unto you that one mother is more honorable than a thousand virgins.

Then said John, who had also been among the people, Behold, others of them say that thou art indeed the son of Joseph, but that Joseph is of the royal line of King David. What sayest thou to this?

Of what Jesus spake concerning his birth

And Jesus answered, Lo, the one party maketh of my mother a harlot, and the other party maketh of my father the descendant of an adulterer and murderer.

Albeit Joseph the carpenter is a slow and foolish man, and albeit he hath cast me off utterly, yet am I prouder to be his son than the son of such a king as David.

Then lastly said James unto him, Behold, the people say that thou wast not born in Nazareth but in Bethlehem; for needs must the Messiah be born in Bethlehem, according to the prophets. Tell us the truth now concerning this also.

Jesus answered unto him, Lo, they will not even respect the place of my birth. But if the truth cometh from Bethlehem, they will receive it; but if it cometh from Nazareth they will not receive it.

Verily, the folly of men passeth belief.

Ere long, methinks, they will say perchance that Kings of the East came to worship about my cradle with gifts of gold and frankincense, or that the very angels of heaven announced my birth unto men!

*Of what
Jesus spake
concerning
his birth*

For they think that the truth is tested by signs and wonders, rather than that all signs and wonders are tested by the truth.

But I say unto you: Hold fast to the truth; for though heaven and earth pass away, yet the truth shall not pass away.

Then Jesus was silent. Yet I saw well that the disciples understood not his words, but yearned in their hearts to believe the tales which they had heard among the people.

For it was in vain that Jesus taught them. Their souls were marked unto superstition from their mothers' wombs.

CHAPTER XXXVI

Now Jesus went about among the people, teaching, and doing deeds of healing among them.

Of the defeat of Jesus at Jerusalem

And there were brought unto him upon the sabbath day twain that were sick of a grievous disease, and he healed them.

But the priests and the Pharisees said unto him, Behold, why dost thou on the sabbath day that which is not lawful?

Jesus answered, The sabbath was made for man, and not man for the sabbath.

And they said unto him, But it is not lawful to heal on the sabbath day.

And he answered, Is it lawful to do good on the sabbath day, or to do evil? To save life, or to kill?

Then the chief priest spake with indignation, and said unto the people, There are six days in which men ought to work: in them therefore come and be healed, and not on the sabbath day.

Jesus said unto the priests, Who are ye, that ye speak thus? And they answered unto him,

Of the defeat of Jesus at Jerusalem

fellow, stood forth, and said, How if I love not my neighbor, and take no joy in him? Show me whence cometh this joy.

Jesus answered unto him, Can one born blind be shown the joy of the light, or one born in a dungeon know the blessing of the free air? Let him first see the light or taste of the air, then shall he know of its blessing.

But the fellow would not be silent, but spake yet again, Behold, to fulfill the Law is easy in comparison with the yoke which thou wouldst lay upon us. For whatsoever case ariseth, we can bring it in our minds before the Law of Moses and decide thereby. But under thy teaching we must needs judge every case by itself to do justice therein.

Jesus answered unto him, Even so. My yoke is not easy, nor is my burden light. Whatsoever things one gaineth easily, and without effort, are not worth the gaining.

Then the chief priest saw that his moment was come, and he spake yet once more, saying, Yea, but if ye obey not the Law of Moses, ye shall be scourged and imprisoned during this life, and suffer in hell during the life to come.

But what penalty cometh upon you if ye heed not the words of this stranger? Let him speak.

Of the defeat of Jesus at Jerusalem

And all the people were silent; and Jesus, also.

Then the people, when they saw that he was silent, cried out unto him, Speak, if thou art a prophet! What punishment cometh upon us if we heed not thy words?

Jesus said unto them, Alas, my children, ye shall remain even as ye now are.

Then the people laughed him utterly to scorn, and laid hold upon him, crying, The man is an impostor! Let us stone him! But others said, Let us thrust him from the edge of the rock outside of the city, that his bones may not pollute the city.

And they led him away, while the priests silently withdrew, that they might not be accused of his blood. And we followed, as though amazed, among the throng where they led him, even to the verge of the cliff that overlooketh the Valley of Jehoshaphat.

Then I remembered the place; and I tripped up the feet of two of them that held Jesus, and we and the disciples escaped from among them, and fled down the cliff unto the

*Of the de-
feat of
Jesus at
Jerusalem*
cave that had sheltered me many years before when I came from the wilderness.

And we were hidden in the cave all that night until the pursuit was past.

CHAPTER XXXVII

A<small>ND</small> the next morning Jesus said unto me, Lead thou the way into the wilderness.

Of the change that came over Jesus in the wilderness of Judea

Then I threw myself upon the ground, and entreated him, saying, Bid me rather lead the way unto Antioch, and I will bring thee thither in safety though it be many miles. There thou canst preach the gospel among the Gentiles, for perchance they will believe.

But go not out into the wilderness. It is a stony place, a place begirt with fire, where we shall lie down among thorns, and our tongues shall be parched with drought.

In the wilderness man becometh hard as the rocks about him; he forgetteth to smile, and his soul burneth up with a zeal barren as the fruitless earth that burneth his feet.

Go not out into the wilderness, dear Master.

But Jesus answered unto me, Others will preach unto the Gentiles; I was not sent unto them, but unto mine own people.

They have rejected the wine that I brought them, yet the wine was good; I must find other ways to bring it unto them once more.

*Of the
change that
came over
Jesus in the
wilderness
of Judea*

Behold, I have learned the wisdom of the fig-tree and the olive, and that of the soft rushes which whisper together beside the Sea of Galilee; but it availed not.

Let me now learn the wisdom of the briar and the thorn, and the wisdom of the rock heated by the sun like to a coal in the furnace.

Let me learn the wisdom of the wilderness. And I thought, There is no wisdom in the wilderness, save the wisdom of the Serpent, and that he is in no mood to learn. Nevertheless, as I was bidden, I led the way.

And we abode many days in the wilderness. A ring of burning brass seemed to bind my brain, and my spirit was heavy with dread of what would come.

And Jesus began to be changed. He chose to be much alone, his face was other than that of aforetime, and he no longer smiled

One while, when the disciples murmured because of the terrors of the wilderness, he would rebuke them shortly, and another while he would blame bitterly himself for that he had failed among the Jews at Jerusalem.

I was sent to do the will of my Father, he said, and I knew not how to do it. Lo, I am an unprofitable servant.

148

Then I questioned with myself whether his soul were not sick, and one day I said to try him, Master, why speakest thou of God as the Father?

Of the change that came over Jesus in the wilderness of Judea

For the Greeks, among whom I lived, are wont to speak of the Earth as their mother. And that seemeth to me right and fitting, and a beautiful habit of speech.

We are sprung from the loins of the Earth, and she giveth us suck, and though here, indeed, her breasts be dry, yet elsewhere are they flowing with milk; she beareth us as children upon her bosom, and at the last her arms are enfolded around us forever.

Why then speakest thou of God as the Father?

Jesus answered unto me, Because a father chasteneth his children.

I said unto him, Nay, Master, if ever thou dost spread thy gospel over the earth, be assured that men will worship the Mother rather than the Father. For the Mother is a higher symbol than the Father.

Jesus said unto me, Judas, beware lest the Father chasten thee, even as he now chasteneth me.

And I beheld that his soul was sick, and I remained full sorrowful.

CHAPTER XXXVIII

THEN came messengers unto Jesus from John the Essene, that was baptizing by Jordan.

How Jesus was baptized of John the Essene

Now I knew little of this John, but that little was more than enough.

For he had sent, while we were in Galilee, a word of rebuke unto Herod the Tetrarch for that he had taken in marriage Herodias, the divorced wife of his brother Philip.

And whatsoever Herod's motives in that may have been, I held that John was a meddler in what concerned him not.

And I remembered the Essenes full well from the days of my youth, so that I knew what manner of man he was.

Thus, when Jesus said unto us, We will go down unto Jordan to meet with John, I answered unto him,

Master, thou knowest that I wished not to come out into this wilderness; yet would I remain in the wilderness forty years rather than go down unto Jordan to meet with this John.

Jesus said unto me, Judas, thou art false unto thine own teaching. For Jordan is the

151

fairest of streams that bear water through this land; and water is the source of life. Is it not the sap that runneth through the branches of trees, and is it not the blood that runneth through the veins of men?

To bathe in Jordan ought to bring thee great delight.

Yea, Master, I answered, Water is good, and to bathe in Jordan is good, but why meet with John?

But Jesus answered, I say unto you, John is a prophet, and more than a prophet. So we got us down unto Jordan.

And John was even such a man as I had thought, clothed in camel's hair, with a girdle of skins about his loins, and he looked like one whose meat is locusts and wild honey.

And there was a great crowd about him, unto whom he preached, saying, O generation of vipers, who hath warned you to flee from the wrath to come?

For now the ax is laid unto the root of the trees: therefore every tree which bringeth not forth good fruit is hewn down, and cast into the fire.

I indeed baptize you with water unto repentance: but he that cometh after me is mightier than I; he shall baptize you with the Holy Ghost and with fire.

Whose fan is in his hand, and he will thoroughly purge his floor, and gather his wheat into the garner; but he will burn up the chaff with unquenchable fire.

And the people wept, and confessed their sins, and were baptized of him in Jordan.

And to my sorrow I beheld Jesus going forward with the rest to be baptized of John.

But John forbade him, saying, I have need to be baptized of thee, and comest thou to me?

Jesus answered unto him sadly, Yea, for men have rejected me as one of no authority; henceforth let me speak at least with the authority of him baptized of the prophet John.

Now when Jesus was baptized and came up out of the water, a white dove flew down from one of the trees, and alighted upon his shoulders.

And all the people took it as a sign; and Jesus said unto me, Judas, did I not hear a voice from heaven saying, This is my beloved Son in whom I am well pleased? Didst thou not hear such a voice?

And when I shook my head sorrowfully, Jesus was seemingly disturbed; and he left us,

How Jesus was baptized of John the Essene

153

*How Jesus
was bap-
tized of
John the
Essene*

and went up alone into a mountain on the other side of Jordan.

And I thought, The dove is the gentlest of all living things. Can Jehovah have corrupted even the dove?

CHAPTER XXXIX

THEN I followed after Jesus up the mountain, and my heart was desperate with fear.

And, albeit unused to pray, I prayed then unto Satan, the great Serpent, the spirit of wisdom, the friend of my youth, that he might appear, and save us in our extremity.

And Satan knew me as of old, and said unto me, Judas, what seekest thou?

And I said unto him, Behold, Jehovah deceiveth Jesus of Nazareth, that was a true prophet, and leadeth him astray upon this mountain.

For he hath deluded him, making him to believe that he is the Son of God.

Go, therefore, ere it be too late, and persuade him with thy wisdom that he is not the Son of God but a man as other men, and save him from the toils of Jehovah.

Satan answered unto me, If the seed hath fallen by the wayside or on stony places or among thorns, there is hope that it may be choked or withered away, but if it hath fallen

155

*How Satan
met Jesus
upon the
mountain*

upon ground fertile for evil in the man's heart, naught can be done.

Howsoever I will speak unto him the words of wisdom.

And Satan came unto Jesus, and, I heard all that which passed between them.

And Satan said unto him, Jesus of Nazareth, thou that wouldst think thyself the Son of God, command that these stones be made bread.

And Jesus was silent; and Satan said unto him yet again: Thou knowest that thou hast no power so to do. But if thou wilt hearken unto my wisdom, men shall learn to make bread grow even among stones, and the waste places of the wilderness shall blossom even as the Valley of Sharon where the roses bloom.

Jesus answered unto him, Man shall not live by bread alone, but by every word that proceedeth out of the mouth of God.

Satan said unto him, Yea, but doth not God speak in the bread which he maketh into nutriment for men's thought, or is God but Jehovah?

And he led Jesus up unto a peak of the mountain, and said unto him, If thou be the Son of God, cast thyself down: for it is written, He shall give his angels charge concerning thee: and in their hands they shall bear thee up, lest at any time thou dash thy foot against a stone.

How Satan met Jesus upon the mountain

And Jesus again was silent; and Satan said unto him: Thou knowest that it is falsely written. But if thou wilt hearken unto my wisdom, in the time to come men shall learn to fly even from this mountain beyond the furthest snows of Hermon or the far-off isles of the sea.

Jesus answered unto him, It is written again, Thou shalt not tempt the Lord thy God.

Satan said unto him, Yea, but is it to tempt God for man to increase in knowledge and power, or is God indeed a jealous god, and his name Jehovah?

And he led Jesus up unto the very summit of the mountain, and showed him the kingdoms of the world and the glory of them,

And he said, If thou wilt hearken unto my wisdom, all these things will I give thee, and thou shalt establish a kingdom ruled by the law of justice over the whole earth.

Jesus answered unto him, Alas, to establish such a kingdom, verily, I would need the power of omnipotent God. Art thou such a God that I may fall down and worship thee?

157

How Satan met Jesus upon the mountain

Then Satan answered unto him, Nay, I am no God, but Satan, the spirit of wisdom.

Jesus said unto him, Get thee behind me, Satan: for it is written, Thou shalt worship the Lord thy God. And if thou art not he, methinketh he may be Jehovah.

Now at those words I gave a great cry, and mine eyes darkened; and when I came unto myself, Satan was gone, but Jesus was standing in the same place upon the mountain.

CHAPTER XL

AND now in the dusk of the evening I heard a mighty voice that seemed to sound in the air above us, saying,

I am the first and the last, without beginning and without end, eternal, omnipotent, omniscient, and omnipresent, indiscernible and incomprehensible:

The Creator of the world, who created the world in seven days, a god of love, yea, and a god of war, known of all my children whom I bless, and abhorrent to all mine enemies who flee my sight forever.

Then when I perceived how these words contradicted themselves, and how they were full of boasting and repetition, I said unto myself, It is the voice of Jehovah.

And despite the growing darkness that obscured all things, I knew that Jehovah was there present with us even as he had been with Adam and Eve in the dawn of time.

And the voice continued, saying, Thou, Jesus, art mine only begotten Son, begotten, not made, being of one substance with thy

159

*How Je-
hovah spake
unto Jesus*

Father by whom all things were made.

Then I shuddered at the blasphemy, but I saw that Jesus listened, and the voice continued, Thou art the Saviour, Comforter, and Redeemer of Men, the Lamb of God that taketh away the sins of the world.

And thou shalt bear this message unto men upon the earth, and it is the message of God.

Blessed are the poor in spirit: for theirs is the kingdom of heaven.

Blessed are they that mourn: for they shall be comforted.

Blessed are the meek: for they shall inherit the earth.

Blessed are the pure in heart: for they shall see God.

Blessed are the peacemakers: for they shall be called the children of God.

And I the Lord say unto you: Resist not evil; but whosoever shall smite thee on thy right cheek, turn to him the other also.

And I the Lord say also unto you, Love your enemies, bless them that curse you,

That ye may be the children of your Father which is in heaven: for he maketh his sun to rise on the evil and on the good, and sendeth rain on the just and on the unjust.

Therefore he that doeth these things shall

be received into everlasting habitations of light, and he that doeth them not shall be cast out into eternal fire.

How Je-hovah spake unto Jesus

Then the voice was silent. And Jesus bowed his head upon his breast, and said, Father, not my will but thine be done. I go down to bear thy message unto men.

But I ran forward, and called unto him, saying, Jesus, thou art betrayed. Knowest thou not that it is a lying voice that hath spoken unto thee?

Then Jesus turned, and said, Peace, blaspheme not! It is the voice of the Lord God!

And he went down the mountain-side, and I was left alone in the gathering darkness with Jehovah.

CHAPTER XLI

BUT my soul was like a mighty fire in the darkness:

How Judas defied Jehovah

For I saw how, through the very goodness of Jesus, Jehovah had found means to betray him, and, in betraying Jesus, had betrayed all mankind.

So that I cried out with a loud voice, and said, O Jehovah, I know thee, and the words that thou hast spoken!

For I know that thou hast sought by them to weaken men utterly and to break their spirit, that thou mayest keep them down in ignorance and sorrow, and rule over them unto all eternity.

And perchance thou mayest succeed for years and hundreds of years, yea, and for myriads of years, yet do I, Judas of Kerioth, defy thee to succeed forever.

Behold, how vain are thy lying threats of hell and promises of heaven to break my spirit even for one moment.

Lo, I say unto thee, that boastest thyself falsely to be God,

Blessed are the mighty in spirit, for in them the true God liveth.

Blessed are they that rejoice, for they shall make others to rejoice.

Blessed are the proud, for pride is the mother of strength.

Blessed are they that seek not after purity, for they shall see truth.

Blessed are the brave, for courage is the greatest good of the soul.

And I say further unto thee that I shall resist evil wherever it be found to the end that evil be destroyed, to the uttermost of my power;

And whosoever shall smite me on my right cheek, I shall smite him with double strength upon the left.

And I shall love my friends and hate mine enemies; for, devoting my whole soul to that in which I believe, whatsoever it may be, I shall strive to make it triumph over them that oppose it;

And if the works that I must do shall be evil, let them be evil, and if good, let them be good, for I shall do that which I must do:

And in this shall I be the child of the Father, that sendeth earthquake and tempest

upon both the evil and the good, and destroyeth alike the just and the unjust.

*How Judas
defied Je-
hovah*

And I curse with a bitter curse all them
that be of thy party, O Jehovah!

Cursed be the poor in spirit, for they help
not themselves but cling about the necks of
others to drag them also into infirmity;

Cursed be they that mourn, for, too weak to
hide their misery in their own hearts, they
must needs force it upon their neighbor, and
make him also miserable;

Cursed be the meek, for there are none such
in their hearts, and those that be so in their
tongues are liars and hypocrites;

Cursed be the pure, for unto the pure all
others are impure;

Cursed be the peacemakers, for they shall
be smitten to the ground of both sides;

And cursed above all be thou, O Jehovah,
and all that preach in thy name!

Then when I had finished, Jehovah trembled so violently that the trees on the top of
the mountains were shaken. And the voice out
of the darkness said,

Judas, thou diest in thy sins; and thy name
shall be a bye-word and a hissing unto them
that come after.

How Judas defied Jehovah

But I spake, and said yet again, Yea, I know that I shall die. But I have lived ere this in the breasts of the true prophets even from the days of Adam and Cain, and I shall live again in the breasts of all the prophets of the future until the end of time.

And these shall understand my deeds, whatsoever other men may say of me.

For they that were one with me in spirit aforetime, they were my fathers in the spirit, and they that shall be one with me in the time to come, they shall be my children in whom I shall live.

Yea, and after long ages I shall still be alive, O Jehovah; yea, long after men shall have arisen in their might and cast thee down and slain thee, O Jehovah, and destroyed even thy memory forever from the face of the earth.

Then I was silent, and awaited an answer.

But none came, save a heavy gobbling out of the darkness, like that of a turkey cock when it disguiseth its fear;

And I seemed to hear a flapping of gigantic wings, as of a great vulture or other obscene bird; and the darkness lifted, and I beheld the stars.

And the peace of the night was all about

me, the night that regardeth not the noisy words of men or of gods.

And I found me a bed of moss and lay upon it, the while I listened to the wind among the tree-tops and gazed upon the stars.

And the peace of the night wrapped me round as in a garment.

How Judas defied Jehovah

CHAPTER XLII

How Jesus promised the keys of heaven unto Peter

Now the next morning I went down again from the mountain, determined still to follow after Jesus and save him, if in any wise it were possible.

And I found him with the disciples at Gilgal, nigh unto Jordan.

And if they welcomed me coldly, yet were there no open words between us. But I, that had been the friend of Jesus before any of the disciples, felt that he was changed toward me. And yet we loved each other, then and always.

Now on the afternoon of that day, Jesus asked his disciples, saying, Who do men say that I am?

And they said, Some say that thou art a disciple of John the Baptist; some that thou art Elias; and others, one of the prophets.

He said unto them, But who say ye that I am?

And Simon Peter answered and said, Thou art the Christ, the son of the living God.

And Jesus answered and said unto him,

169

*How Jesus
promised
the keys of
heaven
unto Peter*
Blessed art thou, Simon Barjona: for flesh
and blood hath not revealed it unto thee, but
my Father which is in heaven.

And I say also unto thee, That thou art
Peter, which name signifieth a rock.

Then Peter interrupted him, and said,
Doth my name indeed signify a rock? I knew
not that. How wonderful!

Yea, said Jesus, and upon this rock I will
build my church; and the gates of hell shall
not prevail against it.

And I will give unto thee the keys of the
kingdom of heaven; and whatsoever thou
shalt bind on earth shall be bound in heaven,
and whatsoever thou shalt loose on earth shall
be loosed in heaven.

Then I looked upon Peter, that dull and
ignorant fisherman, and I thought, Alas, the
seed sown by Jehovah springeth up already
into a crop of foolishness.

CHAPTER XLIII

How the disciples attempted to move the mountain

AND Jesus said unto us, Shortly shall I go up again into Jerusalem. But first must the ground be made ready, and the gospel preached throughout all Judea. Therefore I send you also to preach among the people.

Go not into the way of the Gentiles, and into any city of the Samaritans enter ye not.

But go rather to the lost sheep of the house of Israel.

And as ye go, preach, as ye have heard John preach, saying, The kingdom of heaven is at hand.

Provide neither gold, nor silver, nor brass in your purses,

Nor scrip for your journey, neither two coats, neither shoes, nor yet staves: for the workman is worthy of his meat.

And whosoever shall not receive you, nor hear your words, when ye depart out of that house or city, shake off the dust of your feet.

Verily, I say unto you, It shall be more tolerable for the land of Sodom and Gomorrah in the day of judgment, than for that city.

Now all this saying pleased the disciples, but me it did not please. For from the beginning I had borne the bag in which was our money, inasmuch as Jesus trusted me above the others;

Wherefore I said: Master, thou makest us to be beggars. And when the alms shall be many, these thy disciples will rejoice; but when the alms shall be few, and the disciples begin to be pinched with hunger, they will say unto me, Judas, what hast thou done with the alms?

And they will revile and curse me; for, behold, I know them.

But Jesus hearkened not, for he said yet again, Take no thought for your life, what ye shall eat or what ye shall drink: nor yet for your body what ye shall put on.

Behold the fowls of the air: for they sow not, neither do they reap, nor gather into barns; yet your heavenly Father feedeth them. Are ye not much better than they?

And why take ye thought for raiment? If God so clothe the grass of the field, which today is, and tomorrow is cast into the oven, shall he not much more clothe you, O ye of little faith?

But I said unto him, Master, hast thou so soon forgotten the wilderness of Judea, where the fowls of the air oft perish with hunger, and the grass of the field is burnt up by the sun?

How the disciples attempted to move the mountain

Even in fertile Galilee do not the squirrels put by nuts for the winter, do not the bees provide for themselves honey, and even the little ants gather the grain into the inner chambers of their ant-hills?

Shall we, which be men, show less forethought than the squirrels and the bees and the ants?

Jesus said unto me, Judas, alas, thou hast no faith. And he turned unto the others, and said,

Verily I say unto you, If ye have faith as a grain of mustard seed, ye shall say unto this mountain, Remove hence to yonder place; and it shall remove; and nothing shall be impossible unto you.

Then I beheld that words were useless, and was silent.

But ere we departed upon our journey, I observed how the disciples would steal away secretly, one by one, and go out facing the mountain,

And would stare upon it, knitting their

173

*How the
disciples
attempted
to move the
mountain*

brows, and stretching out their arms, and would speak unto it commandingly.

But I observed not that the mountain was moved.

And one by one the disciples returned, dejectedly.

CHAPTER XLIV

How Jesus met the Syrophenician woman

NOW when Jesus had appointed a meeting place at Joppa by the sea, he sent us away from him to preach.

And wherever I spake unto the people, I said unto them, Obtain knowledge, and do justice unto all men; for knowledge is beautiful and lovely: he that hath knowledge would not receive in exchange for it all the diamonds and gold that are beneath the moon.

Love God, that is life, for in life lieth every blessing. The joy of little children in their play, the joy of young men and maidens in the radiance of love, the joy of manhood in work, and the joy of old age in wisdom: think on these things, and praise God.

Such were the words that I spake, but few hearkened unto me.

And the other disciples, when they preached, said unto the people, Fear the Lord, and repent ye of your sins. For the day is at hand when he shall judge the world, and all them that bow not down unto him shall be cast out into unspeakable fire and torment.

How Jesus met the Syrophenician woman

Repent, repent, repent, for the kingdom of heaven is at hand.

But few be they which shall enter therein; the most part will God in his righteousness cast into everlasting hell.

And multitudes hearkened unto them, and believed their words; so that wherever we went the air was filled with weeping and lamentation.

And when we were come unto Joppa by the sea, we were met once more by Jesus, and henceforth were we with him unto the end.

Now as we went out from the city together, there followed us a certain woman, which was a Greek, by nation a Syrophenician.

And she cried unto him, saying, Have mercy on me, O Lord, thou son of David; my daughter is grievously vexed with a devil.

But he answered her not a word. And his disciples came and besought him, saying, Send her away; for she crieth after us.

And he answered and said, Yea, I am not sent but unto the lost sheep of the house of Israel.

Then came she and worshipped him, for her daughter's sake, saying, Lord, help me.

But he answered, It is not meet to take the children's bread, and cast it unto dogs.

And she said, Truth, Lord: yet the dogs eat of the crumbs which fall from their masters' table.

Then Jesus answered and said unto her, O woman, great is thy faith: be it unto thee even as thou wilt.

And he turned back with her, and healed her daughter.

And I said unto myself, Behold, the words of my Master are become the words of Jehovah, but his deeds are still the deeds of Jesus.

How Jesus met the Syrophenician woman

CHAPTER XLV

Now after that Jesus had healed the daughter of the Syrophenician woman, and was yet
in the city of Joppa, there came one of the
Pharisees, and desired that he would eat with
him. And he went into the Pharisee's house,
and sat down to meat.

And while they were at meat together,
there entered in a woman, richly garmented,
which lived with the Pharisee; and she
brought an alabaster box of ointment;

And she stood behind Jesus, weeping, and
began to wash his feet with tears, and did
wipe them with the hairs of her head, and
kissed his feet, and anointed them with the
ointment.

Then I knew that if I spake, some of the
disciples, which hated me, would say that it
was even because I sought to put money into
the bag, and was a thief; and some, indeed,
latterly have said it. Nevertheless I spake:

And I said unto Jesus, Master, this ointment would have sold for above three hun-

*Of Mary
Magdalene
in sin*

dred pence. Why was it not thus sold, and the money given to the poor?

Jesus answered unto me, The poor ye have always with you, but me ye have not always.

And he bade the woman to stand up; and when she was arisen, behold, it was Mary of Magdala.

And when Jesus looked upon her, he knew her, and said, Woman, art thou yet a greater sinner than when last I saw thee?

Then she wept, and made answer: Yea, Lord. For I returned unto my husband, and he thrust me out, neither would my parents receive me; and I was become a harlot, when this man with whom first I sinned sought me out and brought me hither.

And now will I leave him, and follow after thee, if thou canst save me from my sins.

Jesus answered unto her, Where is thine home?

She said unto him, The home of my youth is in Magdala, and the house of my husband is in Gadara, but they are closed to me. And this man keepeth me not as his wife but as his concubine. I would fain go unto my brother and sister which live in Bethany, but I fear that they also will not receive me.

Jesus said unto her, I will bring thee unto Bethany.

Of Mary Magdalene in sin

But the Pharisee was wroth, and said, Behold, I have loved the woman, and clothed her in garments of purple, and given her all that she asked. Yet now she leaveth me thus.

Jesus answered unto him, Thou shouldst never have sinned with her; meet it is now that thou remain alone and repent of thy sin.

And we went up with her unto Bethany.

And when we came into the town, we met with the sister of Mary, which was named Martha, an unmarried woman that had passed all her years in sad chastity until her countenance was become bitter.

And she began to revile her sister openly for her sins.

And, albeit I thought not too highly of Mary, yet when I looked upon Martha, I said unto her, Mary hath chosen the better part.

For if she in living a natural life hath sinned, thou in living an unnatural life hast sinned the more.

Then the spirit of Martha was rebuked, and she received Mary into the house, where she lived, with Lazarus her brother.

CHAPTER XLVI

Now it chanced at about this time that Lazarus fell grievously sick, and Jesus went up unto their house to heal him, and abode there.

And after many days James the disciple met with Mary of Magdala upon the streets, and she said unto him, He hath healed Lazarus, my brother, after that he lay at the point of death.

And James said unto Peter, Lo, our Master hath brought Lazarus to life even after he seemed a dead man.

And Peter said unto John, Behold, Jesus, our Lord, hath raised up Lazarus who was dead and wrapped in the burial clothes ready for the tomb.

And John said unto the other disciples, A miracle hath come to pass. For Lazarus was dead and laid away in the tomb three days, yet Christ, the Son of God, hath restored him to life.

And they supposed, every one of them, that they had spoken the truth.

Now the days passed, and my heart became

anxious for Jesus, untried in the ways of women, so that I oft visited the house of Lazarus.

And every day when Jesus made ready to depart, Mary said unto him, Stay yet another day and teach us more of thy gospel.

And she sat at the feet of Jesus in a garden of flowers, which was beside the house, and she listened with upturned eyes the while he spake.

But once there came into Bethany a poor harlot that had known Mary of old, and she begged for a crust of bread at the door; and Mary said unto her, Get thee away, thou woman of sin! I know thee not.

Then my soul flamed up within me, and I thought, There be many evils upon the earth greater than a harlot, but none greater than a harlot that hath repented.

And when I went in unto Jesus, I found him alone, and he said unto me, Judas, what thinkest thou? Is not Mary become indeed a good woman?

But I said, Master, Master, knowest thou not why she sitteth at thy feet and gazeth upon thee with upturned eyes?

Because she loveth the word of God, he

said. Because she loveth him that calleth himself the Son of God, I answered.

Of Mary Magdalene in repentance

And it chanced at that moment that Mary entered the room, smiling, and took the hand of Jesus, and sought to hold it in her own.

And Jesus looked into her eyes for a space, then he took away his hand, and went out of the house without a word.

And Mary wept bitterly.

CHAPTER XLVII

AND when I overtook Jesus, he was praying in sorrow of spirit beside the way.

And he said, O Lord, am I indeed thy Son? For I have wasted the hours of the day that was given me to preach the word unto thy whole people;

And I have wasted the word upon a foolish woman that understood it not.

Then we went down unto the disciples, and Jesus said unto them, Prepare ye to enter into Jerusalem upon the morrow.

And Thomas answered and said, Master, ere we enter into Jerusalem wilt thou not speak unto me concerning one thing that hath long perplexed me? Jesus said unto him, Say on.

Then Thomas continued, saying, Master, when first thou taught us, I had thought that thou camest to destroy the Law of Moses. But in these latter days I am in doubt.

Jesus said unto him, Think not that I am come to destroy the law or the prophets: I am come not to destroy, but to fulfill.

Of a discourse upon divorces, eunuchs, and angry persons

187

*Of a dis-
course upon
divorces,
eunuchs,
and angry
persons*

For verily, I say unto you, Till heaven and earth pass away, one jot or one tittle shall in no wise pass from the law, till all be fulfilled.

Whosoever therefore shall break one of these least commandments, and shall teach men so, he shall be called the least in the kingdom of heaven: but whosoever shall do and teach them, the same shall be called great in the kingdom of heaven.

Ye have heard that it was said by them of old time, Whosoever shall put away his wife, let him give her a writing of divorcement:

But I say unto you, That whosoever shall put away his wife, saving for the cause of fornication, causeth her to commit adultery; and whosoever shall marry her that is divorced committeth adultery.

Then the disciples said unto him, If the case of the man be so with his wife, it is not good to marry.

Jesus answered, There be eunuchs which were so born from their mother's womb; and there be eunuchs which were made eunuchs of men; and there be eunuchs which have made themselves eunuchs for the kingdom of heaven's sake.

Then my spirit was hot within me, and I said, Foolish Jesus, because thou hast been deceived in a woman shall we become eunuchs?

Behold, men have learned that it is well for a man to live with a woman. What therefore man hath joined together, let not God put asunder.

Then Jesus turned unto the disciples, saying, Ye have heard that it was said by them of old time, Thou shalt not kill; and whosoever shall kill shall be in danger of the judgment:

But I say unto you, That whosoever is angry with his brother shall be in danger of the judgment; and whosoever shall say, Thou fool, shall be in danger of hell fire.

And all the disciples turned, and gazed at me.

But I controlled my soul and answered, Master, thou, even thou, hast called the Priests and Pharisees fools, and in my presence; but it seemeth to me a small thing to say, Thou fool, in comparison with saying unto one, Thou shalt be in danger of hell fire.

Of a discourse upon divorces, eunuchs, and angry persons

189

CHAPTER XLVIII

A<small>ND</small> the next day we went up unto Jerusalem.

Now the fame of Jesus was grown mighty in the land, owing to the preaching throughout Judea, and the story of the raising of Lazarus, which had gone abroad among the people; so that a vast multitude came forth from the city to meet him, crying,

Blessed is the King of Israel that cometh in the name of the Lord.

And Jesus, when he had found a young ass, sat thereon, and the people went before him, and shouted,

Fear not, daughter of Sion: behold, thy King cometh, sitting on an ass's colt.

And when we were entered into the city, so great was the host about us, that the priests and Pharisees thought best not to show themselves.

And Jesus spake unto the people, and said, All things are delivered unto me of my Father: and no man knoweth the Son but the Father; neither knoweth any man the Father,

How Jesus preached again in Jerusalem

How Jesus preached again in Jerusalem

save the Son, and he to whomsoever the Son will reveal him.

Ye are from beneath; I am from above: ye are of this world; I am not of this world.

I say therefore unto you, ye shall die in your sins: for if ye believe not that I am he, ye shall die in your sins.

Then I plucked his robe, and said unto him, Master, what a word is this?

But Jesus turned away, saying, I thank thee, O Father, Lord of heaven and earth, because thou hast hid these things from the wise and prudent and hast revealed them unto babes.

And the people asked him with one voice, Whom makest thou thyself to be?

Jesus answered, If I honor myself, my honor is nothing; it is my Father that honoreth me; of whom ye say, that he is your God.

Yet ye have not known him; but I know him; and if I should say, I know him not, I shall be a liar like unto you: but I know him, and keep his saying.

Now at the end of the world, the angels shall come forth, and sever the wicked from among the just, and shall cast them into the furnace of fire: there shall be wailing and gnashing of teeth.

And, turning unto us, Jesus said, Verily,

ye which have followed me, in the regenera-
tion when the Son of Man shall sit in the
throne of his glory, ye also shall sit upon
twelve thrones, judging the twelve tribes of
Israel.

*How Jesus
preached
again in
Jerusalem*

Then I cried out unto him, Give my throne
unto Peter, that he may have two thrones, if
he desireth them. For as to me, I desire no
throne.

But all the others asked him, eagerly,
When shall these things be? And what shall
be the sign of thy coming and of the end of the
world?

Jesus answered unto them, Verily, I say
unto you, This generation shall not pass away
till all these things be fulfilled.

When ye therefore shall see the abomination of desolation spoken of by Daniel the
prophet standing where it ought not, ye shall
know that the time is at hand.

And Thomas said unto the rest, What
meaneth Jesus by the abomination of desolation? But the other disciples, although they
knew no more than he, yet made as if they
knew, and Jesus spake again, saying,

Then shall appear the sign of the Son of
Man in heaven: and then shall all the tribes
of the earth mourn, and they shall see the

*How Jesus
preached
again in
Jerusalem*
Son of Man coming in the clouds of heaven with power and great glory.

And before him shall be gathered all nations; and he shall separate them one from another, as a shepherd divideth his sheep from the goats.

And he shall set the sheep on his right hand, but the goats on his left.

Then shall the King say unto them on his right hand, Come, ye blessed of my Father, inherit the kingdom prepared for you from the foundation of the world.

Then shall he say also unto them on the left hand, Depart from me, ye cursed, into everlasting fire. And there shall be wailing and gnashing of teeth.

And they shall go away into everlasting punishment, but the righteous into life eternal.

Then when Jesus was silent, all they that heard him trembled and wept.

And when I beheld many even of the Greeks and Romans among them that wept, I said unto myself, Now is Jehovah's triumph indeed complete; for his worship will spread over the whole earth.

CHAPTER XLIX

AND in despair I said unto myself: Can nothing then save Jesus whom I love? Can naught avail to turn him from Jehovah?

And a mad thought came into my bewildered heart. What if I should deliver up Jesus unto the priests? That he would look to Jehovah for his help, I doubted not. And that Jehovah would fear to stir even a little finger in his behalf, I doubted not. Would not then Jesus behold Jehovah with washed eyes?

And yet it seemed to me but a mad thought, and I would not look it in the face.

But nonetheless it kept plucking at my heart.

Then toward evening Jesus led us out from the city into the Garden of Gethsemane hard by the Mount of Olives; for he had marked my countenance, and sought occasion to speak with me in private.

And as I went with him my soul was exceeding sorrowful, for I knew that the end of all things between us was at hand.

And when we were come into the Garden

195

How Jesus answered the threat of Judas

of Gethsemane, Jesus sent away the other disciples, and he and I were left alone together.

And he said unto me: Speak, Judas.

Then I spake unto him and said, Master, it is the last time that I may call thee so.

For rememberest thou the words that I said unto thee upon that first day, now more than three years ago, when we stood together by the wayside, nigh unto Nazareth?

Did I not say, Let me follow thee, for I believe that the god whom thou proclaimest will destroy Jehovah?

Jesus answered, Yea, I remember. Say on.

And I said, Now may I follow thee no longer. For Jehovah himself is become thy god.

Behold, thou dost corrupt the people, teaching them to avoid evil, if they avoid it, through fear, and to do good, if they do good, through hopes of heaven.

Thus hast thou destroyed among them all love of the good for its own sake.

And I say unto thee, If thou art not prevented, this thy teaching will spread throughout all lands.

And the church which thou wouldst found upon so shaky a rock as Peter will yet be

196

founded firm upon the iniquity of men's hearts.

How Jesus answered the threat of Judas

For men will revile and persecute one another in thy name, and say all manner of evil falsely for thy sake;

They will wage war upon knowledge wheresoever it be found, they will torture them that believe not after their own ways, they will burn the prophets of the truth;

And the earth will be black with ignorance and red with blood for years, and hundreds of years.

That this might be prevented gladly would I give up my own life.

Jesus answered, Yea, and if this thing should come to pass, better were it for me never to have been born.

But this thing will not come to pass, nor canst thou, Judas, prevent me from continuing my teaching among men.

For behold, the priests and the Pharisees will soon themselves receive the teaching, yea, the priests of God will understand his ways.

Then I knew that he was deceived beyond the help of words, and I said unto him, How if the very priests of Jehovah should take thee

and punish thee, and he permitteth it? Would
that destroy thy faith in him?

Jesus answered unto me, My Father will
not permit me to fall into evil, for he watch-
eth over me.

But I said, How if I deliver thee up this
very night unto the priests?

For I knew that they feared to take Jesus
during the daytime because of the people, but
that they would take him gladly at night.

Then Jesus looked upon me sternly and
said:

Judas, thou art eaten up with envy and
jealousy: envy of me, for that I win men to
me whereas thou drivest them away from
thee; and jealousy of all the other disciples,
because though ignorant men they have the
gifts of faith and love which thou lackest.

And thou dost alway give a good name to
thy deeds, to thy past deeds, and to that which
even now thou art planning.

But I answered, hotly: I care nothing for
the name. A deed tells its own tale. And if by
my deed thou art saved from thy folly, I care
not whether the mere name of it be good or
evil.

Then Jesus answered, more gently:

Be it as thou wilt. Yet, even though it be

love that constraineth thee, nonetheless do I dread the event.

How Jesus answered the threat of Judas

Then my heart bounded within me, and I shouted, Ha! thou dost shrink from the test. For thou knowest that in the hour of danger Jehovah will skulk away and betray thee.

Nay, Judas, thou mistakest, Jesus answered softly. Thou mistakest grievously. Jehovah will never forsake me. And, in the event, thy deed will redound greatly to his glory, but, I fear me, to thine own everlasting shame.

Howbeit, when thou seest him stretch forth his right arm to protect me, perchance even thou wilt believe, O my Judas of little faith.

Then he smiled at last, and stretched forth his hand to me, saying, Deliver me up if thou wilt, and thou shalt see what the Lord doeth.

And I bent over his hand, shuddering. And I murmured, Yea, we shall see.

CHAPTER L

THEN we rejoined the other disciples, for I still hoped where no hope was to avoid this deed, albeit that it seemed unto me the one way to bring Jesus again into a right mind concerning Jehovah.

For I knew well that Jehovah would do naught to protect him.

And I knew also that the priests had no authority to put him to death; wherefore I thought that they would perchance punish him lightly, and let him go elsewhere. For I dreamed not of their giving him over unto the Romans.

Nevertheless I still sought to postpone the deed.

And we went with the disciples to sup, in a house not far from the Garden of Gethsemane.

And as we did eat, the disciples spake loudly of their love for him. And Jesus answered, Verily I say unto you that the one of you that hath loved me the most, the same shall betray me.

201

*Of the Last
Suppper*

Then were they all very sorrowful and began every one of them to say unto him, Lord, is it I? And Simon Peter, which had somewhere found a sword, unsheathed it, and said unto Jesus, Point out to me the man that shall betray thee!

Then I spake also and questioned, Master, is it I? He said unto me, Thou hast said.

But Peter, when he beheld that I was the one, sheathed again his sword quickly.

And he said unto Jesus, Lord, what is this betrayal that cometh upon thee?

Jesus answered unto him, Whither I shall be led thou canst not follow me.

Peter said unto him, Lord, why cannot I follow thee? I will lay down my life for thy sake.

But despite these words, Jesus knew the man, and he said, Wilt thou lay down thy life for my sake? Verily, verily, I say unto thee, The cock shall not crow till thou hast denied me thrice.

But Peter spake the more vehemently, If I should die with thee I will not betray thee in any wise. Likewise so said they all.

But Jesus cut short their protestations, and turned and said unto me, That thou doest, do quickly.

Now no man at the table, even after all that had passed, knew for what intent he spake this unto me, so dull and foolish were they.

Of the Last Suppper

And I went out alone into the night, to betray him that I loved into the hands of them that I hated.

CHAPTER LI

AND I went away, into the city, unto Caia- *How Jesus*
phas, the high priest, and offered to bring *was de-*
his men where they might find Jesus. *livered up*
unto the
Priests

And Caiaphas, which was an haughty one,
said unto me, Lo, I will give thee thirty pieces
of silver, as if I had bought a slave of thee.

And I answered, Then if thou buyest him
with money, after thou hast questioned him
wilt thou sell him unto me again for money,
if I so desire?

Caiaphas answered, Yea, for the same
thirty pieces of silver; for I value the man in
truth at something less than thirty pieces. And
he confirmed it with an oath, and swore by
Jehovah. So I accepted the money.

Then were gathered together a number,
with swords and staves, from the priests and
elders of the people; and we went out by the
light of torches, and came upon Jesus with
the disciples, walking among the trees in the
Garden of Gethsemane.

And when I beheld Jesus, something smote

within me, and I went up and kissed him, and said, Hail, Master, yet again!

And the priests and elders came about us. Then Peter, indeed, drew his sword: but he was an awkward man and knew not the use of the weapon, so that when he struck with it he but smote off the ear of one of the servants among them.

Then he dropped the sword, and fled away; and the other disciples, also, forsook Jesus, and fled. And he was led away unto the house of the high priest.

But now after Peter saw that he was not pursued, he recovered from his fear, and followed them afar off.

And when they had kindled a fire in the midst of the hall, and were set down together, Peter came in, and sat down among them.

But a certain maid beheld him as he sat by the fire, and earnestly looked upon him, and said, This man also was with him. And he denied, saying, Woman, I know him not.

And after a little while another saw him, and said, Thou art also of them. And Peter said, Man, I am not.

And yet a little after, another confidently affirmed, saying, Of a truth this fellow also was with him: for he is a Galilean, and his speech agreeth thereto.

How Jesus was delivered up unto the Priests

Then Peter, at the moment when it most behooved him to keep silent if he wished to save himself, began to curse and to swear, crying out, I know not this man of whom ye speak.

And immediately, while he yet spake, the cock crew; and Jesus turned and looked upon him.

Then, methinks, Peter remembered how that he had said unto him, Before the cock crow thou shalt deny me thrice.

But the faces of them about him were threatening, so that he went out hastily.

CHAPTER LII

Now all the remainder of the night I walked to and fro, and wrestled with myself.

For a voice spake in mine ear, saying, Behold, if thy Master taught falsely, and yet taught what seemed unto him the truth, had he not the right so to do?

Art thou, O Judas, even like unto the priests, which demand that all men think as they think?

Then would another voice say, Yea, this is an evil; but that Jesus should have spread the worship of Jehovah over the whole earth were a greater evil. And perchance he may now be saved from Jehovah through thy deed.

And neither voice would be silent for the other.

But as soon as it was day the elders of the people and the chief priests and the scribes came together and led Jesus into their council.

Now I knew not what passed in the council, but soon a rumor ran about the streets

Of the trial and condemnation of Jesus

Of the trial and con-demnation of Jesus

even that Jesus was to be given over to the Romans under an accusation of death.

Then I forced my way in unto Caiaphas, and brought him again the thirty pieces of silver and yet thirty more, and said unto him, Fulfill now thy word, and release Jesus unto me.

But Caiaphas answered, How shall I release Jesus unto thee? For he hath been given over to the Romans under an accusation of death, and is now in the hands of Pilate.

Then I said unto him, Ye have sinned in that ye have betrayed the innocent blood.

But Caiaphas answered, What is that to thee? See we to that.

So I cast down the pieces of silver at his feet, and went out from his presence.

Howbeit I feared not yet greatly; for I deemed that Pilate would not dare to condemn him whom all the people loved.

And I went thence unto the judgment hall, and by means of my knowledge of the Greek tongue, which is honored among the Romans, I obtained admission into the judgment hall; and I beheld there Jesus and the chief priests and Pilate.

And Pilate said unto the priests, What accusation bring ye against this man?

They answered and said unto him, If he were not a malefactor, we would not have delivered him up unto thee.

For we have a law, and by our law he ought to die, because he made himself the Son of God.

Pilate answered, Am I a Jew, to concern myself with such things as these?

They said unto him, Yea, but he calleth himself the King of the Jews. If thou let this man go, thou art not Caesar's friend; whosoever maketh himself a king speaketh against Caesar.

Then I beheld that Pilate was inclined in his mind toward Jesus, for he said unto him, smiling, Art thou the King of the Jews?

But I beheld also that Jesus yet relied upon the aid of Jehovah, for he made answer, Thou sayest it.

To this end was I born, and for this cause came I into the world, that I should bear witness unto the truth. Everyone that is of the truth heareth my voice.

Pilate said unto him earnestly, What is truth? Jesus answered, Hereafter shall ye see the Son of Man sitting on the right hand of power, and coming in the clouds of heaven. Pilate made answer, Alas, is that thy truth?

Of the trial and condemnation of Jesus

Then I arose, and said unto Pilate in the Greek tongue, Thou knowest that these Jews have a custom that at the passover some malefactor of their race should be set free.

Speak unto them therefore, and they will ask that the life of this Jesus be spared.

For I knew not that the priests had been busy all day among the people with bribes and persuasions, and that they had wrought them to the pitch of demanding the death of him whom but yesterday they had accepted as the Son of God.

But when Pilate went out unto them, and said, Will ye that I release unto you Jesus of Nazareth, they all cried out in answer, Not him but Barabbas.

Now this Barabbas was a robber and murderer, which at that time lay in the prison.

Pilate saith unto them, What would ye then that I do unto the other?

And they all with one accord made answer, Crucify him! crucify him!

Then Pilate was incensed, and said unto them, Shall I crucify your king? The chief priests answered, We have no king but Caesar.

And there began to be a tumult in the streets, because that Pilate would not crucify Jesus at once; and he feared an insurrection.

So that he said, Behold, this people is become mad with their prophets, and Sons of Man, and Sons of God, and Gods!

Of the trial and condemnation of Jesus

Shall Rome suffer, so that I may protect one madman against a race of madmen? My duty is to Rome.

And he delivered Jesus unto the Jews to be crucified.

Howbeit he wrote a title and had it placed upon the cross. And the writing was, Jesus of Nazareth, the King of the Jews.

Then said the chief priests of the Jews to Pilate, Write not, The King of the Jews, but He said I am King of the Jews.

Pilate answered unto them, with Roman pride, What I have written, I have written.

CHAPTER LIII

THEN they led away Jesus, my Master, to be scourged. And after, the soldiers put on him a scarlet robe; and when they had platted a crown of thorns, they put it upon his head, and a reed in his right hand: and they bowed the knee before him, and mocked him, saying, Hail, King of the Jews.

And they spat upon him, and took the reed, and smote him on the head.

And after that they had mocked him, they took the robe off from him, and put his own raiment on him, and led him away to be crucified.

And when they were come unto a place called Golgotha, where the hillside is formed into the likeness of a skull, they raised him up upon the cross.

And all they that passed by reviled him, wagging their heads, and saying If thou be the Son of God, come down from the cross.

And I, I sought among the people even for the disciples, to share my heart with them,

Of the death of Jesus

Whether it be well or ill for the world that Jesus died as he died, that the centuries alone can tell.

But my vanity is not so great as to deem that I could in aught transgress the laws of the Unknown God which moveth us to do all that we do.

And I would that every murderer and every traitor had as clear a conscience as mine own:

For I loved my Master whom I slew, nor would I have betrayed him but that I loved even more the truth;

And if I betrayed my Master, yet have I never betrayed the truth.